Dear Reader

I first thought of writing the story of a pair of false teeth when I was on a camping holiday in France. While my family were on the beach, I sat outside my tent and wrote *The Great Denture Adventure* as a poem.

Later, I thought it would be better as a big picture book. In the end, I wrote it out as the story you are about to read.

I have a secret dream that one day it might be made into a massive Hollywood blockbuster film, starring Tom Cruise and Jennifer Lopez with Dame Judi Dench as Grandma. I haven't decided who will play the teeth yet.

Since the book came out, readers have told me other real-life stories about false teeth. Someone's dad lost his in the sea. Another reader's mum found some teeth in the washing machine and – here's the spooky bit - no one knew whose they were.

So, if you happen to be travelling with an adult who has false teeth, do not lend them this book.

They might laugh. The teeth might fly out of the window. You will then have to stop the train and it will be really, really embarrassing.

Terence Blacker

Have you discovered the brilliant Ms Wiz stories by Terence Blacker?

Ms Wiz is the world's most popular paranormal operative (you must never say she's a witch). She goes wherever magic is needed with Herbert, her amazing talking rat. And the children of St Barnabas School find themselves zapped into sixteen fantastic, funny adventures.

'The trouble is,' Ms Wiz says, 'Magic and being a serious grown-up don't seem to go together.'

Titles in the Ms Wiz series

1. Ms Wiz Spells Trouble
2. In Stitches with Ms Wiz
3. You're Nicked, Ms Wiz
4. In Control, Ms Wiz?
5. Ms Wiz Goes Live
6. Ms Wiz – Banned!
7. Time Flies for Ms Wiz
8. Power-Crazy Ms Wiz
9. Ms Wiz Loves Dracula
10. You're Kidding, Ms Wiz
11. Ms Wiz, Supermodel
12. Ms Wiz Smells a Rat
13. Ms Wiz and the Sister of Doom
14. Ms Wiz Goes to Hollywood
15. Ms Wiz – Millionaire
16. The Secret Life of Ms Wiz

Terence Blacker

The Great Denture Adventure

Illustrated by Tony Ross

MACMILLAN
CHILDREN'S BOOKS

For India Tickner – T.B.

First published 1992 by Macmillan Children's Books

This edition published 2003 by Macmillan Children's Books
a division of Macmillan Publishers Limited
20 New Wharf Road, London N1 9RR
Basingstoke and Oxford
www.panmacmillan.com

In association with Virgin Trains

ISBN 0 330 39742 7

3 5 7 9 8 6 4

A CIP catalogue record for this book is available from the British Library.

Typeset in Palatino by SX Composing DTP, Rayleigh, Essex
Printed and bound in Great Britain by Mackays of Chatham plc, Kent

CHAPTER ONE

It All Began With a Sneeze

It all began with a sneeze. Not the polite little "Achoo, oh, excuse me everybody" that you or I might make, but a giant of a sneeze, a sneeze to end all sneezes, Supersneeze.

It was Sunday afternoon and my brother Tom and I were at Grandma's for tea. Outside, the sun was shining and we could hear the sound of people in the park. When our mum and dad came to collect us after tea, we would have all gone for a walk out there – if it hadn't been for that sneeze.

Grandma had just brought in a plate of rock cakes. "I cooked them yesterday especially for you children," she said.

Tom and I looked at one another. The problem with Grandma's rock cakes was that they tasted like rocks.

"After you, Tom," I said. My little brother was eyeing the chocolate biscuits, so I added in a quieter, more threatening voice, "Rock cakes before biscuits."

"What was that, Jane?" asked Grandma.

"I was just telling Tom not to eat too many cakes," I said loudly. "All right, Tom?"

Grandma smiled with pleasure.

"Sometimes I think you only come

here for my rock cakes," she said.

"They're Jane's favourites," said Tom.

I was just about to reply when I noticed that Grandma had a rather peculiar look on her face.

"Ah," she said loudly.

There was a moment's pause. Then she said it again.

"Ah."

"Um, ah what, Grandma?" I asked politely.

"*Ah.*" Her eyes were closed now and she was frowning, as if she were trying to remember something. "*Ah.*"

"Grandma?" I was a bit worried now.

"Ah. *Ah.* Ah. *Ah.*" Her nose twitched and she began flapping her hands helplessly like a chicken trying to fly.

"Are you all right, Grandma?"

"Ah. *CHOOOOOOOOOO*!!!"

The sneeze, when it came, was like a hurricane sweeping through her sitting room. Rock cakes were scattered everywhere. Cups and saucers went flying. As for Grandma, she was lifted clean off her seat.

And it seemed to last for about ten or twenty seconds. When it was over,

Tom and I looked at our grandmother in total astonishment.

"Wow," said Tom eventually. "Better out than in, eh, Grandma?"

Grandma had gone quite pale. "Oh," she was saying. "Oh, phwear."

"Bless you, Grandma," I said kindly. It was then that I noticed that she looked different somehow. Her face seemed to have changed shape.

"My phweeff," she said eventually through wobbly lips. She pointed to the window. "My phweeff gom."

For a moment, I couldn't understand what she was talking about. Then I realised what had happened.

"Oh no," I gasped. "Her teeth seem to have flown through the window!"

Tom looked at me as if I were mad. "All of them? They just . . . fell out?"

"They're dentures, dummy. False teeth."

Tom ran to the window.

Was it possible? As Grandma sat there, her eyes wide in shock and the colour returning to her face, I thought back to the Supersneeze. There had been the deep breath. Then the blast-off. And, yes, something white and gleaming *had* seemed to whistle past my left ear, across the room and out of the window.

"Where are they?" I asked.

"I think they're in the park," said Tom.

"My phweeff!" cried Grandma. "I want my phweeff back!"

And that was the start of the Great Denture Adventure . . .

CHAPTER TWO

"Good News and Bad News . . ."

"Good news and bad news, Grandma," Tom called to us from the window. "The good news is that I can definitely see your teeth. The bad news is that they've been caught by a seagull."

Grandma and I hurried over to the window. "It must have thought they were a piece of bread," I said.

"I wonder what false teeth taste like," muttered Tom.

Grandma was staring into the park making an odd yodelling sound that I've never heard before or since.

"Other seagulls are chasing it," Tom continued. "The one that's got them is diving and swooping. It's dropped them!"

"Aphter vem!" cried Grandma, making for the door.

Tom and I followed. If we could just reach the park before anyone found the dentures, all would be well.

But, by the time we had crossed the road and run into the park there was a very sizeable problem. Just where we had seen the teeth land, a rather large couple, a man and a woman in matching tracksuits, had decided to take a rest. Right now they were stretched out in the sun, breathing heavily – and Grandma's false teeth had disappeared.

"Oh no, joggers," I muttered to Tom.

"Giant joggers," he added unhelpfully. "If they're running to lose weight, they've got a long way to go."

"Speak to them, Grandma," I said urgently as we stood nearby. "Explain that they're lying on your dentures."

"Can't schpeak wivout phweeff."

"They probably won't be long," said Tom.

So we sat and waited . . . and waited.

After about five minutes, the joggers heaved themselves on to their feet and lumbered off. We hurried to where they had been lying and looked down at the grass. The dentures were nowhere to be seen.

"I'm sure they were here," I said. "Perhaps someone picked them up."

"Gross," said Tom under his breath.

"*Wook*!" Grandma was pointing in the direction of the joggers. "My phweeff!"

And there they were – stuck, as if by glue, to the red, wobbling tracksuit of the male jogger, just where he had been sitting.

"My phweeff are phwtuck to vat man's vottom!" shrieked Grandma.

Tom winced. "Are you sure you still want them, Grandma?" he said.

But Grandma was already in pursuit. "After vem, children," she gasped.

Now Tom and I are quite good runners but the joggers were covering the ground surprisingly quickly. By the time we reached the main road, they were thirty metres in front of us. We could hear, some way behind us, Grandma shouting at full volume.

Then disaster struck. The joggers turned into the High Street. My brother and I put on a burst of speed but, by the time we had reached the corner, they had disappeared.

"There are about five roads leading out of the High Street," I said. "They could have taken any of them."

Tom suggested we split up. "You go right and I'll go left. We'll meet up in ten minutes."

I grabbed him by the shoulder. He may be the most annoying person in the world but he is my brother and he's too young to be roaming the streets alone looking for teeth.

"We stick together," I said firmly, as Grandma joined us, red-faced and puffing heavily. "After all, what's more important – a child who could get lost or a pair of missing false teeth?"

"My phweeff," said Grandma firmly. "Vere are lots of children vut I've only got one fet of phweeff."

"Grandma!" I protested.

"See you here in ten minutes," said Tom, and he was gone.

Some surprising things had happened that day (and worse was to come) but I still say that nothing – not the Supersneeze, not the seagull, not

the attachment of the teeth to a jogger's bottom – absolutely nothing surprised me as much as the fact that ten minutes later, almost to the second, Tom was back at the crossroads. This is possibly the first and last time my brother has been on time in his whole life.

"Any phweeff?" asked Grandma.

Tom shook his head.

"Sorry, Grandma," I said. "Perhaps we should give up and go home. Mum and Dad expect us back—"

It was at this moment I noticed that Tom was staring over my shoulder down the street. "It's the wobbles!" he shouted suddenly. "They're coming back."

And there they were. Pad, pad, puff, puff, down the High Street towards us. Pad, pad, puff, puff . . .

As they passed, Grandma, Tom and

I craned our necks and looked eagerly at the man's bottom.

"Honestly," said his friend disapprovingly. "Some people just *have* to stare, don't they?"

"Oh dear," I said, as the joggers huffed and puffed away from us. "They seem to have gone."

"One toothless bottom," said Tom gloomily.

"Now what do we do, Grandma?" I asked.

"Poleeph," said Grandma. "Go to poleeph phtation."

I saw a telephone box nearby. "I think I'd better ring Mum and Dad to tell them we're going to be late home."

CHAPTER THREE

"You're Doing *What*?"

"You're doing *what*?"

My mother's voice goes quite strange when she's surprised. She can sound like a cartoon character, all squeaky and hysterical.

"I said we're just helping Grandma to find her teeth."

"Her teeth? Did you say her teeth, Jane?"

"Yes, they've come out and sort of

disappeared."

"Have you looked under the sofa?"

"No, we went to the park. Then we followed some joggers but the teeth seem to have dropped off so we've got to go to the police station."

I heard my mother muttering something to my father about Grandma and sherry.

"Can I speak to Grandma?" she asked eventually.

"You could," I said, nodding as Grandma tapped her watch impatiently, "but she can't speak to you."

"*What*?"

"She can't speak to anyone, Mum. I thought I told you – she's lost her teeth."

"But—"

"Better run now, Mum. See you later."

"Wait—"

I hung up. It's not nice to put the phone down when your mother's talking but this, after all, was an emergency.

CHAPTER FOUR

"Excuse Me, This is Not a Joke"

"Excuse me, this is not a joke," I said to the constable who was standing behind the desk at the police station. The more Tom and I tried to explain about Grandma's missing teeth, the funnier he seemed to find it.

"Of course not," said the policeman, trying to keep a straight face. "And where exactly were the dentures in question last seen?"

Tom and I looked at one another. This was going to be difficult.

"Actually," I said with my most serious face, "when we last saw them, they were attached to a jogger's" – I hesitated – "to a jogger's posterior region."

It was too much. False teeth the policeman could just about take, but the combination of dentures and a jogger's bottom finished him off.

He gasped. He wheezed. He went red. He clutched his sides. He—

"My phweeff!"

There was a crash behind us as Grandma burst into the police station. She had heard the laughter from outside and was so angry that she had forgotten her embarrassment at not being able to speak properly.

"It's vot phwunny!" she said, as the policeman gulped nervously.

1000

"Sorry, madam," he said. "I was under the impression that this was, you know, something of a wind-up."

In reply, Grandma smiled very slowly, revealing a wide expanse of pink, naked gums. It was a truly terrifying sight.

"I see now that I was mistaken," said the policeman faintly.

"Thank you very much," I said.

"Now would you care to make a note of where the teeth were last seen?"

Ever since the story of the Great Denture Adventure was reported in the local papers, I've heard of some strange places where false teeth have been found. But no one's dentures, I'm sure, have travelled quite like Grandma's did. They just kept on moving. They had a sort of dental wanderlust.

It can have been no more than an hour between the moment when we last saw them, wobbling into the distance on the jogger's bottom, and when the news came through on the police computer that they had been sighted.

This was not the good news that you might think.

"There's a report of some teeth

fitting the description of your grandmother's missing appurtenances," said the constable, whose name, we discovered, was PC Jones. "They're at the local zoo in some sort of cage."

"Wow," said Tom. "They've locked up Grandma's teeth to stop them escaping."

PC Jones looked more closely at the screen of his computer. "The cage belongs to something called the Great Siberian Mountain Tiger," he said. "Apparently it's not very friendly."

"*My phweeff*!"

The policeman shook his head. "Best to leave them there, I'd say. They can be vicious brutes, them Great Siberian Whatsanames." He glanced at Grandma, who looked as if she were going to give him her toothless grimace again.

For about five seconds, PC Jones considered the situation.

On the one hand, there was a Great Siberian Mountain Tiger. On the other, there was Grandma. It was just a question of which was less frightening.

"Oh well, it's only a big cat, after all," said PC Jones. "Who wants a ride in a police car to the zoo?"

CHAPTER FIVE

"He's Very Big, Very Rare and Very Mean"

"He's very big, very rare and very mean," Mr Kite, the zookeeper told us as PC Jones, Grandma and I hurried past polar bears, snakes, monkeys and owls on the way to the tiger's cage.

I couldn't help noticing that Mr Kite had a large scar on his arm.

"How on earth did the teeth get here?" I asked.

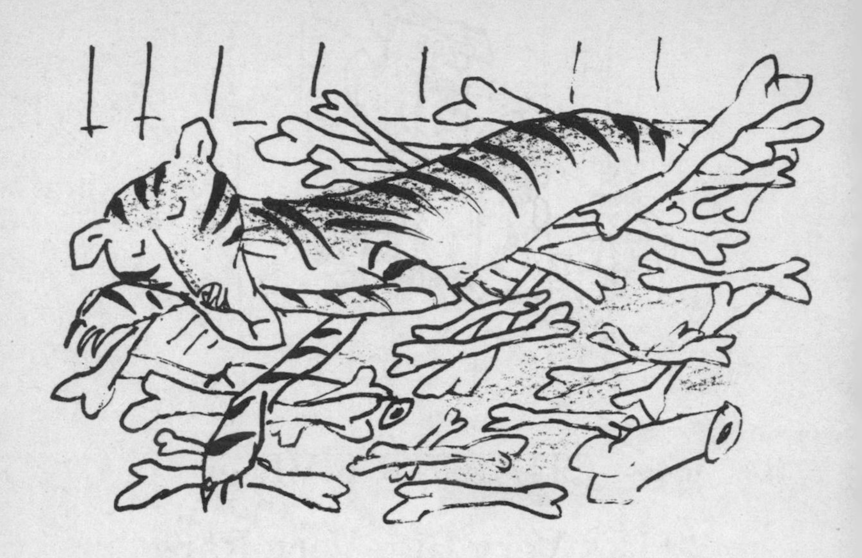

"The local butcher brings us some bones every day," said Mr Kite. "Maybe a dog picked up the teeth and left them in the butchers. Or perhaps the joggers stopped for a nice Sunday roast or—"

"Vet *on* viff it," said Grandma.

At last we came to a great cage with a dark cave in the corner. Fast asleep in a corner was an enormous tiger.

"There are only ten of them beauties

in captivity," said Mr Kite. "We're trying to save him from extinction."

"He doesn't look very grateful," said Tom, and I must admit that, for a change, my brother was right. The tiger looked a bit like Mr Watts, our maths teacher, at nine o'clock on the first Monday of term.

"He can look how he likes," said Mr Kite. "He's an endangered species."

Grandma pointed to a pile of bones

in the corner. "My phweeff?" she asked nervously.

"Hmmm." Mr Kite took a closer look. "Yes. Could be bones, could be gnashers. Hard to tell, really. Of course, if it was in the wild, the Great Siberian Tiger would not normally give a pair of dentures a second look. His favourite meal is . . ."

"Never mind the nature lesson," said PC Jones, stepping forward. "There's only one endangered object round here that interests us – and that's them teeth."

Shrugging, the zookeeper picked up a long pole and poked at the pile of bones in the corner. "I can't see any dentures here," he said eventually. "I'm very much afraid he must have eaten them."

Grandma had gone very pale. Her lips began to quiver as if she were about to cry.

Tom, as usual, managed to make the situation worse. "Never mind, Grandma," he said cheerfully. "Just think – your teeth have helped an endangered species survive."

It was at that moment that we heard the sound of guitar music drifting over to us from a bandstand nearby. There were whoops and claps and the sound of stamping feet.

"Spanish dancers," sniffed Mr Kite. "Call themselves Los Crazy Bandaleros. They're meant to be getting the crowds in. Bloomin' racket if you ask me."

Gloomily, we wandered towards the bandstand. We could see flamenco dancers, whirling and turning. As we approached, the clapping and the sound of castanets grew louder.

"Bloomin' castanets. Clack-clack-

clack," muttered Mr Kite. "My animals hate all that noise."

I noticed that Grandma was staring at Los Crazy Bandaleros with great interest. In the back row of the dancers stood a little girl, stamping her feet and laughing with a pair of pink castanets in her hand.

I couldn't believe my eyes. I looked more closely . . .

CHAPTER SIX

"Those Aren't Castanets, They're Teeth!"

"Those aren't castanets, they're teeth!" I cried.

"You're absolutely right," said PC Jones. "That little girl at the back – she's clicking a pair of dentures. As soon as them there Spaniards have finished their act, we'll get 'em back."

It must have been a good ten minutes of general prancing about and stamping of feet before the dancers took a bow and dived into a tent behind the bandstand. Grandma hurried after them, followed by Tom, me, Mr Kite, with PC Jones bringing up the rear.

The entrance to the tent was blocked by a big man with a squashy nose and small eyes.

"Er, olé, olé," he said gruffly. "Adios amigos."

"I beg your pardon?" I said.

"Gracias . . . Arreviderci . . . Amo amas amat . . . Viva y Spania."

"What's he on about?" asked Tom.

"Scrammo, mush. Comprende?"

I gasped. "You're no more Spanish than I am," I said.

"Qué? You what?"

PC Jones stepped forward. "It is my duty to inform you," he intoned, "that you may be guilty of impersonating a

Spaniard. One more 'olé' out of you and it will be down to the station."

"Strewth," said the man, talking in a normal accent, "I'm only doing what I was told, ain't I? I was supposed to stop people getting in while the rest of 'em got away."

"What's your name?" asked PC Jones, taking out his notebook.

"My name's Pedro." We all looked at him suspiciously. "Well, Pete actually, but everyone calls me Pedro."

"What about the Bandaleros?" I asked. "Where do they come from?"

"Er, Stepney," said Pedro. "Every night, we hire the costumes from Larry's Loony Emporium and olé . . ."

"I warned you," said PC Jones.

"Sorry, Officer. Because I can't dance or play the guitar, my job is to hold up members of the public who want to meet the Bandaleros until they've scarpered off back to the fancy dress shop to return the gear."

Grandma pushed past him and looked in the tent. "Vey've gom!" she cried despairingly. "Vere was a vack entranph."

"Abracadabra," said Pedro, adding quickly, "that's not Spanish by the way, Officer."

"I'll deal with you later," said PC Jones. "We require a pair of pink castanets that one of your troupe was using. We have reason to believe that they are in fact missing dentures."

"They must be on their way to Larry's Loony Emporium," said Pedro.

"How are we going to find this emporium place?" I asked.

"Pedro's going to take us there," said PC Jones. "Aren't you, Pedro?"

It was a squeeze in the police car

with Grandma, PC Jones, Mr Kite, Pedro, Tom and me but somehow we all fitted in. It wasn't long before we reached a very odd shop, hidden away in the back streets of the town. In the window were all sorts of masks and jokes and funny costumes and above the door was a sign which read:

We opened the door which made the sound of a lavatory flushing as we entered.

A man with long grey hair and a false nose stood behind the counter. He took one look at us as we stood there seriously and said, "Sorry, we don't cater for funerals." He laughed to himself. "Only kidding. What can I do you for?"

PC Jones stepped forward. "Cut the funnies, Larry," he said grimly. "We are on the trail of some missing dentures. I have reason to believe that you may be able to assist us with our enquiries."

Larry clapped his hands enthusiastically. "Brilliant," he said. "That's the best fancy dress act I've seen all day."

"I am not a fancy dress act," said PC Jones with great dignity. "I am a police officer. Kindly show me to your false teeth."

"Teeth," muttered Larry, reaching

BAD
FIDO
WHooPee

under the counter. He took out some joke dentures and put them on the counter. They jumped up and down and made an odd chortling sound.

It was at that point that Grandma pushed her way from the back of the group to the counter. She looked grimly gummy. "*My phweeff*," she said. "*Now*!"

"All right, all right. Keep your hair on, missus," said Larry. "You'd better come to the Teeth Room."

He led us to the back of the shop where he opened a cupboard. There, gleaming in the darkness, was every size and shape of false teeth imaginable.

"They *must* be here," muttered Tom.

"We're looking for a set of teeth returned by Los Crazy Bandaleros," I explained. "They were picked up at the zoo by one of the child dancers and returned to you by mistake."

Larry was frowning. "Yes, I thought they were strange-looking castanets," he said. "But the funny thing is they went straight out again with a lady who was going to the big Fancy Dress Ball at the Town Hall tonight."

"What's funny about that?" Tom asked.

"Everything's funny," said Larry, pulling a red rose out of his ear.

None of us laughed.

"The question is," I said, "how do we get to the Fancy Dress Ball?"

"Oh, that's easy," said Larry.

And, for the first time that night, he wasn't joking.

CHAPTER SEVEN

"Have You Ever Been an Ugly Sister, Madam?"

"Have you ever been an ugly sister, madam?" Larry asked Grandma.

There was an angry spluttering noise from Grandma.

"Not that you're ugly yourself," said Larry quickly. "But if I gave you the best fancy dress in my shop and you went as one of the Ugly Sisters from Cinderella, no one would think of asking you for your ticket and you could find your teeth at the dance."

Grandma looked doubtful.

"I could come as Cinderella," I said. "Tom could be Boots, the scullery boy."

"Guess who gets the starring role as usual," muttered Tom.

"Perhaps—" PC Jones seemed to be blushing. "Perhaps I could go to the dance as the Laughing Policeman."

"And I could be a jungle explorer," said Mr Kite.

"I'll be a clown, of course," said Larry. "But we'll need another Ugly Sister."

We all turned to Pedro.

"No, not me." He backed towards the door. "Please not me."

Larry was pulling a huge purple dress out of a cupboard. "Just your size," he said. "You'd look really nice in this."

Pedro shook his head firmly. "I am not dressing up as a woman and that's final," he said.

PC Jones stepped forward. "Pedro," he said firmly. "In the name of the law, I command you to get into that dress."

"Oh, all right," said Pedro grumpily.

An hour later, we arrived at the ball. We were such an astonishing sight that, when we stepped out of the police car, no one at the door dared ask for our invitations.

"Wow," said Tom as we saw some of the costumes being worn. Nuns were dancing with highwaymen, Frankensteins were queueing for food beside Donald Ducks. I saw Batman holding hands with Little Bo Peep.

"My phweeff," said Grandma, looking around the room like a hunter searching for her prey.

"Let's spread out," I said. "Once we've found Grandma's teeth, we can enjoy ourselves."

"Why's it so full?" asked Tom.

"There's a rumour that the Duke of Bloomsbury is going to judge the fancy dress," said Larry.

"The Duke of Bloomsbury!" gasped Pedro who, thanks to Larry's efforts, was looking uglier than ever. "He's a cousin of the Queen, isn't he? Quick, someone – how does my make-up look?"

"*Phweeff*!" said Tom and I at the same time.

We looked everywhere.

"Is that them?" asked Tom, pointing to a little tiara on a fairy's head.

"Grandma's mouth isn't that big," I said.

Just then there was a roll of drums and in walked the Duke and Duchess of Bloomsbury.

"I'm vewy honoured to be judging this fancy dwess competition," announced the Duke, a tall man with a permanent smile on his face. "Now please form a line on each side of the dance floor and I'll inspect each costume before deciding the winners."

There was quite a bit of jostling as we took our places. Then, slowly, the Duke began to make his way down the other side of the dance floor, looking carefully at each fancy dress, now and then pausing to say something to one of the guests.

He looked at Batman, the Leaning Tower of Pisa, the fairy, Charles II, Donald Duck, a skeleton with a strange and revolting earring . . .

A strange and revolting earring! That was it!

"Grandma," I whispered urgently.

"Look at the lady in the skeleton suit. On her ear."

"My . . . phweeff," said Grandma and I thought for one moment she was going to cross the dance floor and grab them then and there.

"Better wait until after the competition," I said quickly. "We don't want to cause a scene."

The Duke was walking slowly down our side of the dance floor. He stopped at the Laughing Policeman, looked at him carefully and shook his head. "No," he muttered. "You look much too silly to be a policeman."

"But I *am* a—"

"Sshh!" hissed Tom who was standing next to him.

The Duke looked Tom up and down, then moved on to Grandma. As he paused in front of her, Grandma smiled. This was a mistake.

For a few seconds, the Duke stared at her pink, naked gums. He seemed to go quite pale. "Ye gods, the woman's got no teeth," he murmured to himself before readjusting his smile and turning to me.

"Ah, Cinderella," he said. "Better give the prizes out before midnight, eh, what?"

"Yes, sir," I laughed politely.

When he had finished the inspection, the Duke of Bloomsbury stood in the middle of the dance floor and announced his verdict.

"I shall declare the wesult," he said, "in weverse order. Third is the vewy owiginal Leaning Tower of Pisa." The tower tottered forward to collect its prize.

"Second is Little Bo Peep. Vewy pwetty." A middle-aged woman skipped across the dance floor to collect her prize.

"And the winner," said the Duke, "is the vewy amusing Lady Skeleton."

"*What*?" I gasped.

The woman with Grandma's teeth dangling from her right ear gave a little shriek and ran up to collect her prize.

It was then that I decided to take action. I hadn't chased all over town to see my grandmother's teeth helping

someone else win a fancy dress prize. I marched straight up to the Duke and said, "Excuse me, sir."

A surprised silence descended on the room.

"Cindewella?" The Duke laughed nervously. "You have a wish?"

"Yes, I do," I said loudly. "My wish is that this lady removes her earring and allows it to be returned to where it belongs."

There were murmurs of surprise among the other guests.

"And where might that be?" asked the Duke, with a hint of impatience in his voice.

"In my grandmother's mouth."

"Nonsense," said the woman skeleton, nervously fingering the teeth. "I hired this earring from a perfectly respectable joke shop. The girl's only saying this because she's jealous she didn't win the competition."

"Sir," I said, turning to the Duke, "I can prove it. These dentures will fit only one person. And that person is here tonight."

"You mean . . ." The Duke smiled. "Just like the stowy of Cindewella and the glass slipper?"

"Something like that," I said.

"Oh, goody." He took the teeth from the woman's skeleton ear and leant forward to ask me quietly, "D'you think they ought to be washed first?"

I thought of where the teeth had been that night – from the seagull to the jogger, from Larry's Loony Emporium to the Fancy Dress Ball. "It might be an idea to run them under the tap," I said.

When the teeth were returned, shining brightly, the Duke of Bloomsbury held up his hand.

"If there is anyone in this Town Hall," he announced, "who can lay claim to the dentures I hold in my hand, may that person pwesent herself herewith heretofore to me at the aforesaid undermentioned and, er, sort of wight now if possible."

Grandma stepped forward. There was silence in the ballroom as she made her way, her eyes staring longingly at the false teeth, to where the Duke was standing.

"My phweeff," she said, falling to one knee before the Duke.

She opened her mouth.

The Duke, after checking that they were the right way up, placed them carefully in Grandma's mouth.

A perfect fit.

The place erupted in applause. Even the Duke joined in the cheers as Grandma gave the biggest, toothiest smile of her life.

Then, almost as if nothing had happened and we were still back at home eating rock cakes, she said, "Right, Cinderella and Boots. Pumpkin time. It's time for bed."

Tired but triumphant, we said goodnight to Larry and to Pedro and Mr Kite and to the Lady Skeleton (who was allowed to keep the prize) and were driven back to our parents' house in PC Jones' police car.

"What on earth has been going on?" Mum asked, when she opened the door to us.

"They'll explain," said Grandma. "I'm being given a lift home now by PC Jones."

She hugged us both and whispered, "Thanks, children."

"Well," I said, after the front door closed. "It's a bit of a long story."

And Tom and I sat down and tried

to tell Mum and Dad all about the Great Denture Adventure and why exactly we were so late home.

I'm not sure they believed a word of it. I can't think why not.

THE RIGHT WAY TO WRITE YOUR OWN CV

John Clarke

Whilst care is taken in selecting Authors who are authoritative in their subjects, it is emphasised that their books can reflect their knowledge only up to the time of writing. Information can be superseded and printers' errors can creep in. This book is sold, therefore, on the condition that neither Publisher nor Author can be held legally responsible for the consequences of any error or omission there may be.

Typeset in 11/13pt Times by Letterpart Ltd., Reigate, Surrey.

Printed and bound in Great Britain by Cox & Wyman Ltd., Reading, Berkshire.

The *Right Way* series is published by Elliot Right Way Books, Brighton Road, Lower Kingswood, Tadworth, Surrey, KT20 6TD, U.K. For information about our company and the other books we publish, visit our website at www.right-way.co.uk

CONTENTS

For Jenifer

INTRODUCTION

While many people have a vague idea of how to put a CV together, those who have taken pains to ensure that theirs is as professional-looking as possible are much more likely to be invited to an interview. Although some valuable advice is available, many so-called 'experts' offer poor-quality CV consultation, either over the Internet or through the small ads – usually at a price. Just about anyone with access to a computer can create a great-looking CV, so why should you pay out for something which, with the help of this book, you can do *better* yourself?

Although this book is bound to help some more than others, anyone currently in the job market can learn something of value from it. The purpose of this book is to provide an easy-to-follow guide. I do not claim that it will overcome all the problems. No book could. Each one of us is unique, and nowhere is that fact more clearly displayed than in a bundle of CVs where the career patterns of people who have worked in the same trade or profession can be infinitely variable. At the end of the day, your CV will be as individual as you are – hopefully, with the use of this book, you will be able to present your unique experiences and talents in the best possible way. In the end it comes down to being as sure as you can be that your CV is a **concise**, **factual** and **attractive** document.

First, carefully read the book right through. Then, return to the beginning and start composing your CV. Read a bit and do a bit, then read a bit more and so on, to the end. Once you have finished, and are happy with the end result, it is a good idea to let someone else have a look over it, even if only to check for spelling or typing mistakes. But danger lurks. The urge to criticise is an innate facet of human nature, and the chosen party may not feel happy in returning the documents with little or no comment. The possible consequences are obvious and potentially destabilising. Try to choose someone whose opinions are worth having, but who is not a close acquaintance. This will minimise the risk of intrusion by the individual's emotions and make an objective appraisal more likely. If you are a student, one of your teachers or lecturers would make an ideal 'proofreader'.

1

PLANNING AND PRESENTING YOUR CV

What should my CV look like?

Views vary about the layout of a CV – no two CVs will look alike. The design of your CV will ultimately reflect your personality and your suitability for the job for which you are applying. For example, an Accountant's CV will be a far more serious-looking document than that of an Entertainer, who may use stylised typefaces, colour and perhaps incorporate a photograph.

Should I use a computer?

The use of a computer in the creation of a CV is expected: if you do not have access to a PC at home or work, most local libraries offer low-cost computer facilities of which you can make use. Having your CV available on disk means that it can be altered easily, at any time, and can be cheaply reproduced – either by printing one out or e-mailing one off, as and when required. Many people, particularly those working in the fast-changing IT and Media industries, keep a copy of their CV on a disk or on their PC at all times, and update it as any change in their work status or experience occurs, whether or not they are actively seeking a new job.

Writing style

Jargon

There is a growing tendency by people and organisations in all walks of life to speak and write in pretentious jargon instead of making clear, simple statements. This is 'gloss culture', which has spread out from its origins in the world of advertising to infiltrate the whole of the public services sector and large areas of industry and commerce, with devastating consequences. If you allow the gloss culture to creep into your CV, you are in grave danger of being identified with its two main objectives, i.e. the concealment of poor standards and the glorification of mediocrity. Within some industries, however, the use of jargon *is* necessary to show your knowledge of current trends and 'buzzwords', for example in New Media and Marketing careers.

Keeping it simple

It is important to stick to the hard facts and to avoid small-talk, or statements which are merely conversational. Remember that your CV will, initially, get no more than a quick scan, perhaps lasting less than twenty seconds. The impression given by that first acquaintance with the recruiter will decide whether the CV is placed in the small pile for a longer read later, or simply consigned to the wastebin. Elegant flowing prose will impress no-one: the experienced recruiter will see straight through it and toss it aside with contempt. Far better to stick to easy-to-read language presented with accurate spelling and syntax. (If you are not confident in your spelling or grammatical construction, consult the appropriate books and ask a more proficient wordsmith to give your CV a final check before sending it anywhere.)

Keep your writing simple and brief – do not use a

whole sentence when one word will do. Similarly, do not use your CV as an opportunity to show off your extensive vocabulary. The recruiter is unlikely to have either the time or inclination to reach for a dictionary when ploughing through a stack of CVs; you will just make yourself look pretentious.

Use of the First Person

Some people prefer not to use the first person (I/we); however, modern CVs are less rigidly structured than in the past and the use of the first person can make a CV seem more personal and less 'formal' (see page 59). If the job for which you are applying *is* a more traditional position though, you may wish to avoid use of the first person, using the passive voice instead (see page 56). In any case, avoid *overuse* of the word 'I' (I did this, I did that and so on) as this can make the CV seem monotonous and repetitive.

Self-promotion

While many job applicants ruin their prospects by trying too hard and appearing boastful, a similar number wreck their chances by selling themselves short. This 'modesty factor' can prevent you from giving a good account of yourself, or even cause you to be unaware of the many useful qualities you possess. As they say, 'No-one else is going to blow your trumpet, so you'd better do it yourself!' If your level of skill at a certain task is outstanding, say so. Even better, mention the actions of others in response to your achievements. Promotions, awards, rewards, or any other kind of formal recognition of your talents and hard work should be included.

Presentation

Even if the job you are seeking does not exactly match your career background, good presentation might cause the recruiter to say, 'He isn't exactly what we had in mind, but he certainly seems interesting. Let's have him in for a chat.'

Paper

Invest in some good quality, bright white paper. Do not be tempted to use coloured or embossed paper. Your CV may be faxed and/or photocopied at some point, which will further decrease the print quality, so it is best to make the hard copy of your CV as clear and legible as possible, avoiding coloured paper or light-coloured inks which may render the information illegible at a later stage.

Folders

If you choose to put your CV in a folder or binder, bear in mind that it may well be removed (and most likely not replaced) if the recruiter wishes to photocopy or fax the document.

If you do choose to use an A4 'see through' perspex folder with a slim plastic slide binder or some form of spring, spiral or comb binding, you should have a face or front page, in the centre of which should be typed something along the lines of:

CURRICULUM VITAE
OF
(FORENAME) (SURNAME)

When the CV has been inserted securely in the folder, the introductory letter should be clipped to the outside.

Printing

It is important that the printer you use to print your finished product is capable of producing a high quality document, without smudges or blurring. If your home or business printer is not up to the job then, again, try your local library. (Avoid printing it off from one of the company printers, or photocopying it at your current workplace – you are surprisingly likely to be found out!)

Envelopes
Having taken pains to ensure that your finished CV looks pristine, the last thing you want now to do is to fold it up and put it into a standard-sized envelope, which may get trampled on and bent *en route* to your potential employer! Spend a bit extra on a board-backed A4 envelope to make sure that, when it arrives on the recruiter's desk, your CV looks as good as it did when you printed it out.

How long should a CV be?
Many so-called 'experts' will invariably tell you that on no account must your CV exceed two A4 pages. Their advice will be damaging in many cases. The majority of CVs that I have prepared are on three A4 pages. Most of the remainder are on two or four pages, with a very small number exceeding four pages. I personally do not like to see a CV exceed three pages, but this cannot be taken as a hard and fast rule.

Consider the typical example of an applicant who is already in management, and is applying for a better paid job with even more responsibility than at present. He needs to give a comprehensive account of his experience and could well find that keeping down to three pages will do more harm than going onto a fourth.

Faced with a CV on, say, three and a half A4 pages, I have debated the question, 'Do we cut it down, or do we leave it?' with many job applicants, and the answer is not always the same. But there has to be a convincing reason for allowing the CV to encroach onto a fourth page. Applicants in this situation should do their utmost to keep down to three pages, but not by attempting to cram too much information onto each sheet. This leaves the reader hunting around in search of important material and he will lose patience. Do not try to 'cheat' by using small type and narrow margins. This will only make a quick initial scan difficult or downright impossible if the reader is 'visually challenged'.

Online job-hunting

You may find in your job-hunting that you never actually need to print off your CV. The Internet is fast becoming *the* place for recruiters, agencies and applicants to match skills with requirements.

Formats for on-line CVs

Many companies and agencies will insist on your CV being available in Microsoft Word format, as this makes it readily available to be e-mailed to, and opened on, the vast majority of PCs. You should be aware, however, that the recipients of your e-mail may not have the same typefaces installed on their computers, and so your CV may not appear as you intended when they open their attachment. (With some versions of Microsoft Word you have the option to 'Embed TrueType fonts' as you save the document – explore the program's 'Help' menu for more details of how to do this.)

If you are looking for an Internet-related job, it is often a good idea also to have a copy of your CV available in HTML format (the format which a Web browser can display), and perhaps even to put it on your personal home page (see page 23).

CV Banks

Some recruitment websites offer the facility either to upload your CV (usually in Microsoft Word format) to their 'CV

Bank' or to create one online by filling out the site's CV form. In the latter case, it is a good idea to use the Copy and Paste function on your PC to insert the relevant information from your CV document into the appropriate boxes on the website – this will save you time and the bother of typing out the same details over again, perhaps with new spelling or typographical errors included. (Beware, though, when copying and pasting, that some of the formatting of your CV may change in the process; your bullet points or tab spaces, for instance, may disappear.) Your CV may be 'searched' for certain keywords relating to your skills or qualifications, so make sure that any such words (for example, 'MSc', 'Accountant' or 'NVQ', for example) are included on your online CV.

Wordprocessing your own CV

Editing

Many people would say that the major advantage of wordprocessing any document is the facility to 'spell-check' your work automatically. Be *very* careful, though, not to rely on this feature too heavily – many typing mistakes slip past the spellchecker (for example, when you write 'form' instead of 'from'). Often, when you have written something yourself, it is hard for you to see the mistakes you have made because your eyes read what your brain thinks ought to be there. For this reason, it is always best to ask an amply-literate, human friend to check your work after your computerised friend has given it a once-over!

CV templates or 'wizards'

Many wordprocessing software packages (including Microsoft Word and Corel WordPerfect) offer a ready-made CV template which you can use to 'fill in the blanks'. These can be useful if you are not very familiar with the use of a computer, however there is always the danger that employers and recruitment agents may become swamped with dozens of similar-looking CVs, all showing their writers' lack of imagination! If you must use one of these CV templates, do try and alter aspects such as the typeface (font), sizing and/or spacing to make yours stand out from the pile. Also, remember to delete any headings or sections which are not relevant to you – do not just leave them blank! (Many of these programs are intended for the American market, and so will refer to the CV as a Résumé – be sure to change this when applying for a job within the UK.)

Features

Take full advantage of the emphasis which can be made by the intelligent use of CAPITALS, *italics*, **bold** and <u>underlined</u> text. Note the use of the word 'intelligent' – if you use too many of these functions in too great an abundance the CV appears messy and thc impact is reduced. Try to establish a 'hierarchy' of headings. For example: the main headings, such as 'Personal Details' and 'Curriculum Vitae', could be in capitals; sub-headings, such as 'Education' or 'Hobbies', could be in bold text; and information which you want to highlight within the text, such as dates or job titles, could be in italic type. As a rule, try to avoid underlined text as, these days, underlined words tend to look like hyperlinks.

The difference made to a CV by the imaginative and constructive use of wordprocessing tools may be seen in the following first pages of CVs which all show exactly the same information, but laid out in different ways.

Example 1 – The Serviceable CV (Professional)

PERSONAL DETAILS

Full Name:	JONES, Sarah
Address:	101 Heron Road, Anytown, Midshire, XX1 1XX
Home Telephone:	01999 999999
Mobile Telephone:	07999 999999
E-mail:	sarah@anymail.com
Date of Birth:	9th August (year)
Place of Birth:	Anytown, Midshire
Nationality:	British
Marital Status:	Single – no children
Driving Licence:	Current (clean)

CURRICULUM VITAE

Education and Qualifications

Sept. (year) – July (year)	Largetown University, Largetown, Northshire
	June (year), BA Hons History (2:ii)
Sept. (year) – July (year)	Anytown Comprehensive School, Anytown, Midshire
	June (year), 8 GCSEs (1A, 4Bs and 3Cs)
	June (year), 3 'A' levels (2Bs and 1C)

Training

	Acme Media Ltd.
Sept. (year)	Windows 98 (2 weeks)
Nov. (year)	Word 2000 (1 week)
Dec. (year)	Customer Service (2 weeks)

Example 2 – The Sleek CV (Creative)

Sarah Jones 101 Heron Road, Anytown, Midshire, XX1 1XX
Tel: 01999 999999 Mobile: 07999 999999
E-mail:sarah@anymail.com

PERSONAL DETAILS

DOB: 9th August (year)
Place of Birth: Anytown, Midshire
Nationality: British
Marital Status: Single
Driving Licence: Current (clean)

EDUCATION AND QUALIFICATIONS

Largetown University, Largetown, Northshire
Sept. (year) – July (year)
June (year), BA Hons History (2:ii)

Anytown Comprehensive School, Anytown, Midshire
Sept. (year) – July (year)
June (year), 8 GCSEs (1A, 4Bs and 3Cs)
June (year), 3 'A' levels (2Bs and 1C)

TRAINING

Acme Media Ltd.
Sept. (year) – Windows 98 (2 weeks)
Nov. (year) – Word 2000 (1 week)
Dec. (year) – Customer Service (2 weeks)

Example 3 – The Stylised CV (Cheery)

Sarah Jones – Curriculum Vitae

Address:	101 Heron Road, Anytown, Midshire, XX1 1XX
Telephone:	01999 999999
Mobile:	07999 999999
E-mail:	sarah@anymail.com
D.O.B.:	09/08/YY
Place of Birth:	Anytown, Midshire
Nationality:	British
Marital Status:	Single (no children)
Driving Licence:	Current and clean

Education and Qualifications

Largetown University Largetown, Northshire 09/YY – 07/YY	06/YY BA Hons History (2:ii)
Anytown Comprehensive School Anytown, Midshire 09/YY – 07/YY	06/YY – 8 GCSEs (A,B,B,B,B,C,C,C) 06/YY – 3 'A' Levels (B,B,C)

Training

Acme Media Ltd – 09/YY (2 Weeks)	Windows 98
Acme Media Ltd – 11/YY (1 Week)	Word 2000
Acme Media Ltd – 12/YY (2 Weeks)	Customer Service

Example 4 – The Badly Laid-Out CV (Boring!)

Personal Details

Name: Sarah Jones

Address: 101 Heron Road, Anytown, Midshire, XX1 1XX

Home Tel: 01999 999999

Mobile: 07999 999999

E-mail: sarah@anymail.com

D O B: 9th August (year)

Place of Birth: Anytown, Midshire

Nationality: British

Marital Status: Single - no children

Driving Licence: Current (clean)

Curriculum Vitae

Education and Qualifications

Largetown University, Largetown, Northshire
Sept. (year) - July (year)
June (year), BA Hons, History (2:ii)

Anytown Comprehensive School, Anytown, Midshire
Sept. (year) - July (year)
June (year), 8 GCSEs, (1A, 4Bs and 3Cs)
June (year), 3 'A' levels (2Bs and 1 C)

Training

Acme Media Ltd.

Sept. (year) - Windows 98 (2 weeks)

Nov. (year) - Word 2000 (1 week)

Dec. (year) - Customer Service (2 weeks)

Each of the first three example CVs (which can be created using any modern wordprocessing software) is suitable for submitting to an employer – *depending on the circumstances of the job and the individual applicant.*

Example 1 is a fairly traditional CV which lays out the information clearly and professionally, with 'no frills'. This kind of layout tells a potential employer that the applicant is steady, traditional and functional – the kind of person suitable for a client-facing role, such as a Teacher, Bank employee, Accountant, Middle Manager, or any other traditional, 'white-collar' job.

Example 2 shows the same information, but in a more modern and 'sleek' format. The use of an attractive (yet clearly legible) typeface, text boxes and appropriate application of emphasis such as bold or italic text, create an impression of an applicant who is fresh-thinking, creative, vibrant and computer literate. This last quality is particularly important if the job for which you are applying will involve using computers. This CV would be particularly suitable for an application for a job in the IT, Media, New Media or Arts industries.

Example 3 would not be suitable for most serious, professional or office-environment type jobs as the excessive use of stylised typefaces, borders and tables and text boxes creates an impression of an applicant with a laid-back, unprofessional and light-hearted attitude. This kind of CV may be suitable for those working in the Leisure and Tourism, or Entertainment industries, or other jobs which necessitate a cheerful disposition – such as hairdressers or serving staff. It should be noted that, however attractive it may look, the overuse of formatting (text boxes, shading, stylised typefaces and so on) reduces the CV's legibility, especially after photocopying and faxing. This formatting can also increase the document's size in terms of bytes, which will increase the time spent e-mailing or uploading to the Internet. Some websites place restrictions on the size of CV files that may be uploaded to their CV banks, so, as a rule, keep things as simple as you can without risking dreariness.

Example 4 shows the applicant's lack of imagination as regards her CV. The type is very small, which will make it difficult for readers with less-than-perfect eyesight to read. (Aim to use a typeface size which is large enough to be easily-read, but not so large that your CV runs to several pages more than necessary. As a general rule, 12pt type is a good size.) The typeface used is dull and old-fashioned, therefore not showing the applicant in her best light. There is also a lot of blank space left wasted on the page here – this could be better filled with, for example, the beginnings of the applicant's Work History. Clever typesetting will allow a lot of information to be included without making the page seem overly-crowded. The use of tables to lay out information such as your Education (as in the previous three examples) is one way of spreading the text *across* the page, rather than *down* it in one long list. A CV such as this can only really be acceptable if your qualifications and experience are *so* attractive that a potential employer will need no extra incentive to look at the document. Even so, the small type and long, list-like construction may cause the reader to miss a vital piece of information and cast the CV aside with the other rejects.

Photographs

Some people like to include a photograph of themselves in their CV – either scanned in or taken with a digital camera. This can sometimes be acceptable on a CV such as those shown in Examples 2 and 3, where the applicant is applying for a position in a modern, relaxed industry, or one which places importance on the applicant's appearance, but it would not really look 'professional' enough for inclusion in a CV such as Example 1. If you do decide to include a photograph, remember that the scanning-digitisation-printing process may distort your features or colouring (unless you have access to top quality graphics software and hardware). You should also think carefully about whether your image will really be of benefit to your application: if you are stunningly attractive, the CV's recipients may be inclined to reject you out of jealousy (especially those of the same gender), but if you have a face which only your mother could love your potential employer may well find the thought of even sitting through an interview with you stomach-churning! If in doubt, leave it out.

Job-seekers such as Airline Cabin Crew or Entertainers, whose appearance may well be the deciding factor for whether or not they are considered for the job, should enclose a professional photograph separate from the main CV, if requested to do so.

CVs on the Web

Having your CV available via the Internet, on your own personal homepage, can offer many advantages for job-seekers, especially in the IT and New Media industries. By providing the URL (www address) of your CV webpage, recruiters will be able to see an example of your skills straightaway, and they can also revisit the CV (or print off another copy if their first becomes lost or damaged) at any time. An online CV is less of a necessity for applicants within non-technical industries; however, if you have the facility for your own homepage (and the confidence in your IT skills), it may make a favourable impression on your potential employer. Detailed advice on writing HTML (or using Web design software) can be found in relevant books or on the Internet. However, here are a few guidelines to follow:

- Ensure that any hyperlinks on the page are up-to-date (i.e. that the pages they link to are still available). *Do* use hyperlinks: an online CV should be an interactive document, allowing the reader to e-mail you, visit your company or personal website, and visit websites of any other companies/organisations mentioned in the CV (such as clubs or societies mentioned in your 'Hobbies' section), all at the click of a mouse. Remember, when e-mailing a word-processed CV, that hyperlinks can also be added to a Microsoft Word document (choose 'Hyperlink' from the 'Insert' menu and type in the URL or e-mail address).
- Make sure that your HTML code is of a standard which will stand up to close scrutiny by potential employers. If you are unsure of your skills, use web-page creation software such as Dreamweaver.
- Avoid creating a page which will look different under another browser. Differences and incompatibilities can occur when using non-standard HTML tags, when using frames, or when saving wordprocessing documents as HTML – this last is considered very bad form.
- Avoid use of colours which may not be visible when printed out, such as yellow. Also avoid dark backgrounds with light-coloured text as this is difficult to read on screen and may cause printing problems.
- Make use of tables, with or without borders, to make the information as tidy and easy-to-read as possible.
- Don't get carried away – too many images and/or animations will detract attention from the important information on your CV, as well as increasing both the time it takes the reader to download the page and the likelihood of the page 'breaking'.

- It *should* go without saying but, if you include the URL of your home page, do make sure that its content is appropriate. Potential employers may be impressed by an informative, creative and good-looking website, but not by pictures of your friends at the pub – or worse!

2

PERSONAL DETAILS

Once you've decided on the format and layout of your CV, next comes the important part – deciding what to put in it! Your personal details should come first on your CV, so that recruiters can see at a glance who you are and how to contact you, should they want to arrange an interview.

Name

The most important part of your CV! Many people like to make their name really stand out on the CV by using a larger, bolder type than elsewhere, so that it sticks in the recruiter's mind. It is a good idea to put your name on *all* pages of the CV, just in case the pages are separated for photocopying, scanning or faxing.

Contact Details

Where applicable, your home address, home telephone number, work telephone number (if you are able to accept discreet telephone calls at work), mobile telephone number (if you're not), fax number, e-mail address and the URL of your online CV should appear clearly at the top of your CV. Obviously, if you do not have, for example, a fax number, leave this heading out! The more contact details you give, the easier it will be for potential employers to get hold of you.

E-mail

When publishing your CV on the Web (or uploading it to a CV bank), it is advisable to omit your personal contact details (telephone numbers, home address and so on) in favour of an e-mail address – preferably *not* the e-mail address of where you currently work! To guard yourself against unwanted 'junk e-mail' to your usual e-mail account, as well as the risk of your current boss intercepting e-mails from recruiters, you could open a web-based e-mail account solely for the purpose of job applications. This form of e-mail also has the advantage of being accessible from any computer, so you don't have to wait until you get home to check up on your job-hunting progress.

Occupation

If you are only applying for employment in a particular role, e.g. electrician, the personal details section of the CV will contain the firm statement that that is what you are:

Occupation: Electrician – JIB Approved

The purpose of this inclusion is to make the reader aware at an early stage that here is a specialist, and not a jack-of-all-trades prepared to try his hand at anything.

If it is likely that you will be applying for a wide range of vacancies, you may find yourself severely restricted by this inclusion, so leave it out. The Occupation should also be left out if you are including a Profile or Experience in Brief (see pages 67-69).

Date of Birth/Age

If you have easy access to a PC, and are therefore able to update your CV on a regular basis, you may wish to add your age, alongside your date of birth. This will eliminate the need for the reader to test his powers of mental arithmetic. However, remember that companies and recruitment agencies frequently hold CVs on file for many months before making a response, so any ages given may go out of date.

Although of less importance, the entry giving details about the number and ages of your children can also become out-of-date. For this reason, some applicants prefer to give the children's dates of birth only, if at all.

Marital Status

Although it would be illegal for an employer to discriminate against employees who are married, homosexual or have children, many job application forms will ask for details of your marital status, so it is a good idea to add this to your CV. Your marital status is whether you are married, single, living with a partner, widowed or divorced, and how many, if any, children you have. For more information on discussing children in your CV, see page 110.

Next of Kin

Next of kin is a detail which may be needed, particularly if dangerous work or employment overseas is your goal. This is most appropriate in the case of a single, widowed or divorced person. If your next of kin's address and telephone number differs from your own, you may wish to add it here.

Health

Another sub-heading which might not be used in every instance covers your state of health. This applies if physical fitness is likely to be a consideration of more than average importance, e.g. a Physical Training Instructor at a holiday camp, or any post demanding prolonged physical exertion, particularly in climates where extremes of temperature prevail. Ideally, this aspect of the Personal Details will be dealt with by declaring the possession of a current medical certificate. People whose leisure pursuits require them to have regular medical checks might also hold a certificate of fitness:

Medical Certificate: Valid to August (year)

Or, if no medical certificate is available, the entry will read:

Health: Excellent

(Assuming, of course, that the physical state accords with the entry.)

Driving Licence
Showing that your driving licence is clean can say something about you, and not just that you have had luck on your side! If the job being applied for involves using a company vehicle, a clean licence can be a positive advantage. If the licence is *not* free from points, the entry will read:

Driving Licence: Current (full)

– assuming that a full licence has been obtained. (If you only have a provisional licence, it's probably not worth mentioning at all.)

If you have your own car (as opposed to being able to borrow your mother's a couple of times a week), then it is a good idea to mention this. Some employers – particularly those in more rural or cut-off areas – may prefer to employ someone who does not rely on public transport.

Preferred Location
If you wish it to be known that you are prepared to relocate, the sub-heading will read:

Preferred Location:
Prepared to relocate within the UK

Alternatively, if you wish to leave open the question of relocation, but wish to enhance your prospects of an interview, you might say:

Preferred Location:
Prepared to work anywhere in the UK

thus leaving yourself free to state on some future occasion that you will travel home each weekend. However, it is by no means certain that a prospective employer would accept the latter as an alternative to relocation.

If you want to work abroad, you would say:

Preferred Location:
Prepared to work anywhere in the world

Obviously the question of returning home each weekend would not arise in this case!

If you do not want to relocate, under any circumstances, preferring to work within commuting distance, the preferred location should not be used – except when submitting your CV to an online CV Bank, as these will be searched by national, and even international, recruiters, and you don't want to waste your time and theirs with offers of jobs hundreds, if not thousands, of miles away.

Other Details

Try to remember the requirements of application forms relating to your trade or profession. For example, in certain foreign parts an applicant may be required to declare his religion.

The National Insurance number is always an inclusion

when the CV is being used to apply for work offshore. Again, it is a matter of knowing your own field.

If you are registered disabled, this should be entered in the personal details section with details of your disability.

If you have a bi-sexual name (one which can be given to a male or a female), or a foreign or unusual name, you may wish to add a Gender subheading to avoid any confusion.

Overleaf is a list of most of the personal details which any one CV might contain. It goes without saying that few, if any, applicants will require them all. For instance, if you don't have a passport you are not expected to insert the appropriate sub-heading and leave a blank space alongside. Neither should you use the passport subheading if you are not likely to be going abroad in your work.

PERSONAL DETAILS

Full Name:	Chris Smith
Occupation:	Electrician – JIB Approved
Address:	1 The Close, Anytown, Midshire, XX1 1YY
Home Tel:	01888 888888
Mobile Tel:	07888 888888
Home Fax:	01888 777777
E-mail:	chris_smith@anymail.com
Web:	http://www.csmith.isp.com/
Gender:	Male
Date of Birth:	15th February (year). (Age XX)
Place of Birth:	Anytown, Midshire
Nationality:	British
Religion:	Christian
Marital Status:	Married with son aged 11 and daughter aged 6
Next of Kin:	Mrs A Smith (wife) – address as above
Nat. Ins. No:	ZZ 00 00 00 Z
Driving Licence:	Current (full). Have own transport.
Passport No:	888888888 – expires October (year)
Health:	Excellent
Preferred Location:	Prepared to work anywhere in the world.

3

EDUCATION, QUALIFICATIONS AND TRAINING

This section varies from one individual to the next. The way you set out these details, and the amount of space they occupy on the CV, will depend on the level of academic education and/or vocational training you have received, and the extent of your work experience. For example, a recent graduate will place much more emphasis on (and give more space over to) his academic career than will someone who has worked in a profession for many years.

How far to go back

Any CV should include the applicant's education from the age of eleven onward. The name and a brief address (the area and the county/city) of each establishment attended should be included, so offering the recruiter the option to verify your qualifications if desired. If you attended more than one school, give the dates each school was attended. Where an applicant has attended more than two schools (I once had a client who had been to nine), it is standard practice to include only the last two. Many applicants choose to list their education starting from the most recent qualification, going backwards in chronological order, as this shows the reader exactly what standard of education has been reached, without needing to plough through a possibly long list of examinations and certificates.

Listing examinations

Those born before 1972 should give their GCE 'O' Level and/or CSE results, and those born after this date should give their GCSE details. In both cases, any 'A' Levels should also be included. If you choose to include the grades obtained for each individual qualification it is usually most effective to present these lists in descending order of grades. However, where a particular subject is of greater importance in relation to the kind of work being sought, you may wish to begin the list with this subject, regardless of the result.

Letters after your name?

If you are a member of a professional association, the appropriate entry should be made here, e.g.:

Professional Association MCMI

Where this entry is applicable, it is worth considering whether to include the letters of the professional association alongside your full name in the Personal Details section. The same consideration should be given in the case of a degree, e.g. BA. If you do choose to add these letters after your name, ensure that they are listed accurately and in the correct format. For example, if you have received a Master's degree it will effectively 'cancel out' your Bachelor's degree, so, for example, you should *not* add BSc *and* MSc after your name, just the MSc. If you have obtained a doctorate, you may add Dr before your name *or* PhD (or MD or whatever) after your name, not both.

Non-academic training

Over the years, many applicants will have attended short training courses, run either by the employing company or a specialist training organisation. Where these are at all likely to have a bearing on future employment, they could be included at this point on the CV, or even in with the work experience details.

The 5 examples which follow should help you decide which format is best for you, depending on your level of education and work experience:

1. New graduates or final year students (see below).
2. Degree or postgraduate level education with work experience (page 36).
3. HND level education (page 38).
4. Mainly vocational training, with some school-level qualifications (page 39).
5. Solely work experience, having left school with no qualifications (page 39).

1. New graduates or final year students

If you are a new graduate looking for your first job, it is likely that your CV will contain very little work experience, apart from perhaps part-time work. In this case, your academic career will be the decisive factor of your CV, so you should include as much information as is applicable to the job for which you are applying, and detail your education *before* any work experience.

Obviously, the aim here is to economise on space, while still providing the necessary information. If you have an impressive array of GCSE and 'A' level results, in varied and useful subjects, you may like to give full details; if not, merely indicate how many passes were achieved. The thing to remember is that, with each new level of education attained, the former level is superseded: if you have a first class degree in Mathematics, the reader will not really care whether you achieved an A or a D for your GCSE Home Economics!

However, the question still arises of whether or not to give a course breakdown. In making this decision, you have to bear in mind that the syllabus of one institution may vary from that of another, in the same subject. Unless the recipient of the CV has copies of the different syllabuses readily to hand, confusion could arise. As a general rule, you should only include details of modules or courses studied if they are directly applicable to the work for which you are applying. For example, if your main degree is in History, but you studied a module in French for a semester, you might like to include this information when applying for a job involving pan-European trade. The most important thing is to show how your academic pursuits have equipped you with skills transferable to the workplace. So, for example, you may wish to mention how the presentations you researched for and gave in front of your peers have enriched your communication and organisation skills.

EDUCATION AND QUALIFICATIONS

Oct. (year) to June (year)
University of Anyborough, Anyborough
June (year) BA (Hons) (2.i) English Literature
Courses included:
French Language and Literature, Creative Writing and 10,000 word dissertation on the work of Angela Carter.

Sept. (year) to July (year)– Anytown School, Anytown, Midshire
June (year) – 10 GCSEs (grades A – C)
June (year) – 3 'A' Levels:
English (A), French (A), History (C)

2. Degree or postgraduate level education with work experience

Just as, in the above instance, the importance of your GCSE results is lessened when you attain a degree, so too is the importance of your degree lessened by the gaining of some solid work experience. If you have been working at a full-time job for a substantial amount of time (say, over 12 months), then your Education section should be listed *after* your work experience section. At this point in your career, all a recruiter wants to know is that you actually *have* a degree (or a Master's or a Doctorate), and you can indicate this early on by adding the appropriate letters before and/or after your name in the Personal Details section. Now, your Education and Qualifications section is reduced to the bare bones, leaving more room on the CV to detail your work experience:

EDUCATION

Northtown University (year – year)
MSc in Computer Science (Distinction)

University of Anyborough (year – year)
BA (Hons) in Literae Humaniores (2:ii)

Anytown Grammar School (year – year)
June (year) – 3 'A' Levels (grade A)
June (year) – 8 GCSEs (grades A – C)

3. HND level education

In the case of the HND it is necessary to decide whether it would be worthwhile providing details of the course content, listing the subjects covered. Whatever the particular field of endeavour may be, this question will always arise with regard to the most advanced qualification gained, because in most cases the recipient of the CV will have little or no knowledge of the course content.

So what would I do? I would first find out if the applicant possessed a level of practical work experience to match his HND. If he did, I would prefer to leave things as they stand and use the space saved on the CV to expand on his career history, which would precede the education details. If he did not possess an adequate range and depth of experience, I would place the education before the work experience on the CV, and list the units passed straight off the diploma, or its accompanying notification of performance. The need to do this is most common where applicants are young, and have not had the time to develop their careers much. It is sometimes more appropriate to compromise, by listing only the subjects which most closely relate to the kind of job you are applying for, as shown in the example below:

EDUCATION AND QUALIFICATIONS

Sept. (year) to June (year) – Anytown College of Further and Higher Education, Anytown, Midshire

June (year) – HND
– Business and Marketing (Full-time)
The course included: Marketing; Planning and Decision Making; Organisational Structures and Processes; Business Information Systems; Financial Accounting Framework; International Trade Economics

When facing this dilemma, many applicants place photocopies of their certificates and associated documentation in the envelope with their CV. The resulting bulge of unsolicited material is likely to discourage the recruiter, whose desk may already be piled high with the efforts of others. Far better to have an extra page on the CV, which might at least command respect on account of the time and patience that has obviously been required.

Unlike this course, others might require only part-time attendance, e.g. Day Release, Block Release or Evening Classes – state which. For more on HND level CVs, see Example 7 on page 65.

4. Mainly vocational training, with some school-level qualifications

If your qualifications are more vocational than academic, it is likely that you will be applying for a job which places more importance on these 'work' skills than on your learning abilities, and so this vocational training should be given as much weight on your CV as previous examples placed on exams. The work experience ought to be listed first. In the following CV the applicant's further education and training is a mix between civilian and military. Anyone who has served in HM Armed Forces may find the example overleaf helpful.

5. Solely work experience, having left school with no qualifications

Many people reading this chapter will despair at this point because, despite years and years of work experience, they have little in the way of formal qualifications. Take heart. One of the best CVs I have ever written was for an Engineer whose only qualifications were his indentures. Some twenty years previously he had served a five year apprenticeship with an old established company, running

EDUCATION AND QUALIFICATIONS

Sept. (year) to July (year) – Anytown School, Anytown, Midshire

June (year) 3 CSEs:
Technical Drawing (2), Mathematics (2), English (4)

Sept. (year) to June (year) – Anytown College of Technology, Anytown, Midshire

City and Guilds of London Institute
– Heavy and Light Vehicle Maintenance
June (year) Part One Certificate
June (year) Part Two Certificate

(year) to (year) – Royal Air Force (Service Qualifications)

(year) – Education Test Certificate, Part Two
– English; Geography; History

TRAINING

(year) – Instructional Techniques, Forward Reporting, Recruiting, Emergency Services Vehicle Maintenance, Basic Computing.

its own, carefully devised in-house apprentice training scheme. This man, whose achievements were awesome, represented an outstanding example of qualification by experience.

Provided your CV lands on the right desk, all the reader

will want to know is what you have done in your work. This will enable him to decide what you can do for him. (If your CV lands on the wrong desk, it will be read by a 'personnel professional', who might have little understanding of what he is reading. In the absence of a decorative array of certificates and diplomas, he may toss it aside. You could also come to grief at the hands of a recruitment consultant who, until a fortnight earlier, might have been selling baked beans.)

Obviously, your chances will be much better where someone with experience in your trade is involved in the recruitment process. This is more likely where a company does its own recruiting.

If you have no academic qualifications, you must list your work experience first and then present any qualifications you do have (certificates, memberships and vocational courses) as a confirmation of the standards you are able to work to. Do not include school exams which you did not pass.

I would advise any young person with few qualifications to go back into education and study for two good 'A' levels in solid subjects, or a vocational equivalent. These will command widespread respect from prospective employers reading your CV. Many youngsters who have left school early may find the less pressured environment of a sixth-form or technical college is more suited to their personality and lifestyle.

Be wary of the marketing skills of institutions selling a range of alternative courses, some of which are looked upon with suspicion by employers. Before paying out good money for a course advertised in a newspaper, check the credentials of the institution involved and, if possible, ask a careers adviser, or a worker in the industry which you wish to work in, just how much weight such a qualification will carry on your CV.

QUALIFICATIONS

Nov. (year) CITB Advanced Scaffolder's Card
(Reg no: XXXXXX)

Feb. (year) NJC/ECI Registered Scaffolder
(No: XXXXXX)

Aug. (year) Permit User's Certificate
(No: XXXXXX)

June (year) TJIT Offshore Survival Certificate
(No: XXXXXX)

TRAINING

Cann Scaffolding (Anytown) Ltd

Sept. (year) Height Awareness (3 days)

Feb. (year) Health and Safety (1 day)

EDUCATION

Sept. (year) to July (year)

Anytown Comprehensive School, Anytown,
Midshire.

4

CAREER HISTORY

The Career History is usually the part of a CV which most interests the reader. It is also the part which will demand the most of your time, thought and patience.

At this point I must point out that *whatever goes into a CV must be the truth*, since it is a criminal offence to obtain employment by deception. If this still doesn't convince you, the thing to remember is that, if you tell the truth, the whole truth and nothing but the truth on your CV, and you do not get the job for which you are applying, this really is in your best interests. The recruiter knows what kind of person is best suited for the role – if that is not you, don't feel despondent. It is preferable to find a less prestigious job which you can do well, than one in which you are constantly struggling to keep up due to the exaggerated claims of competence on your CV.

Ordering your employment record

As you will see in the examples on pages 55 to 66, your career history should, in most cases, read *backwards*, starting at your current or most recent job. Your present or most recent post will be the one of most interest to the reader, who will want to be able to form an accurate picture of your career path.

For all rules, however, there are always exceptions. It can be a good idea for a young person, such as a school-leaver or new graduate, to show clearly that he started work as soon as he was old enough, rather than having waited until he had no choice in the matter, in which case the Career History will run in chronological order (see Example 1 on page 55).

How far should I go back?

As with many parts of the CV, this will differ from person to person. An applicant who has been working for 30 years in a dozen differently-skilled jobs would be advised only to detail his last ten years of employment to avoid littering the CV with a multitude of unrelated odd-jobs carried out in his youth. On the other hand, a person with fifteen years experience of working in one trade or profession, at six different companies, should include all of these details.

To have had few jobs over a long period of time shows a degree of stability and reliability, although skilled tradesmen who have had numerous employers have usually worked in places far apart and are accustomed to changes in working environment. This, coupled with the broad experience gained, will, in many instances, enhance their prospects (see Example 4 on page 60).

Self-employment

The self-employed generally fall into one of two categories. The first, and perhaps more common, is tradesmen or salesmen working on an hourly or commission basis. Apart from reduced protection under the law, the main difference between this type of self-employment and employee status lies in the method of payment. Duties and responsibilities, time-keeping and the standard of work requirements will not necessarily differ to a large extent. Therefore, the CV will be presented in the usual way.

The second category includes those who have been running their own business. While some prospective employers may be discouraged by the possibility that these applicants might not conform easily to the disciplines of full-time employment, others will be aware that the customer is the most demanding master of all. If long hours in excess of the accepted norm have been worked, week in and week out, this fact should be conveyed, as in Example 8 on page 66. Prospective employers may wonder why your business is not continuing, in which case you might like to make the following inclusion in an accompanying letter:

> Although my business continues to make a satisfactory return, the long-term prospects are uncertain. For this reason, I have decided to seek full-time employment with a well-established large company, strong enough to hold its own in this highly competitive field.

(Assuming of course that this is the case, as it so often will be.)

For guidance on how the rest of the letter might read, see page 112.

What to include

Periods of employment and *unemployment*

You need to show continuity of employment with no unexplained time gaps. Avoid allowing the reader to draw the conclusion that you might have been in prison or had serious health or mental problems for a time. If a period of unemployment took place a few years ago, show it (see Example

2 on page 58). This is particularly important when giving a career history spanning ten years or more. If you conceal this period of unemployment by telling lies, you may in fact be confessing in writing to an offence you have not committed, i.e. working whilst claiming benefits.

If you are currently unemployed, your CV must show this; however, be aware that your chances of securing an interview may be lessened by your status. The advice I would offer you, if you are in this situation, is to go flat out to find a job. Even if this new job does not ideally match what you are looking for, it will get you back on the ladder and provide a firmer platform from which to apply for something more suitable.

If, during your unemployment, you undertook some kind of retraining for a reasonable slice of the period, you may wish to add something along the lines of the following:

> Nov. (year) to Oct. (year)
> Took advantage of this period of unemployment to retrain, with a view to acquiring greater versatility.

(Details of this training will already have been inserted under the Education Section.)

In this way you have shown that you are sufficiently self-motivated to have improved your range of skills in order to get yourself off the 'dole', and this can only count in your favour. Similarly, if your period of unemployment was spent travelling, raising a family or doing voluntary work, do say so – such things add interest to your character and can make for good topics of conversation during your interview.

Periods of imprisonment
If you are currently out of work following release from prison, all you can do is *tell the truth.* I subscribe to the belief that he who is clever enough to tell a lie will be clever enough to know better than to try it. Although it is known for applicants in this situation to make false statements, e.g. long-term unemployment, working for a friend, working overseas etc., the truth could emerge at an interview, or through a prospective employer making a thorough check on your background. Any applicant feeling inclined to attempt concealing a period of imprisonment should remember that *it is a statutory offence to obtain pecuniary advantage by deception.* You are best advised to contend that your debt to society has been paid, and that you intend to apply yourself with great dedication to your career, in order to regain the respect of your fellow citizens.

The Rehabilitation of Offenders Act 1974 was designed to help people in this situation. It gives guidelines on when an applicant is required to tell an employer about convictions. The full Act is too long to quote here, but basically most offences, receiving not more than 2½ years in prison, are 'spent' after a period of rehabilitation. The rehabilitation period for a prison sentence of 6 months up to 2½ years is 10 years; for a prison sentence less than 6 months it is 7 years; and for a fine it is 5 years. These periods are halved if the person convicted was under 17 at the time. When an offence is 'spent', the applicant does not have any legal obligation to tell an employer, even if the employer asks about convictions. If the employer does find out at a later date, he cannot legally take action against the individual.

Certain occupations are exempt from the Rehabilitation Act: Teaching, Medical work, Accounts, Law, Care work (including voluntary posts) and the Gaming and Betting Industry. The Act covers offences which receive fines, probation orders and custodial sentences. There are separate sections for young adults under 17 years of age. You can get advice about the Rehabilitation Act in libraries, careers services and from NACRO, the Crime Reduction Charity (see Appendix, page 123). Before omitting to mention your term of imprisonment, however, remember that you still have the problem of unexplained gaps in your career history.

Dates

For each job, include the date you started and the date you finished working there. If you can't recall the exact starting and finishing dates of your jobs, do your best to put it all together, complete with month and year, for the past ten years. Beyond that, most applicants will not be able to recall much more than the year, especially where many job changes have occurred. Young applicants who list part-time or weekend jobs needn't be too precise about the dates they worked as the reader will understand that the whole working period would have been constantly interrupted by academic pursuits (see Example 1 on page 55).

Addresses

Give the address of each company and state (briefly) what it does. There is no need to add post codes as most people are unable to remember the post codes of past employers. If one of your former employers has gone out of business, do not worry – you are writing a concise account of your career history as it has taken place. The fact that one of your former employers is no longer around is not relevant. The address from which they conducted their business when you worked for them is the address you should use. Alternatively, if they are still in business but have moved to new premises, you could give their current address, if you know it. This is particularly worthwhile if your former employer is likely to give you a favourable recommendation if approached by a prospective employer.

If you are applying for a job in a tightly-knit industry, where your potential employer is likely to know most, if not all, of the companies listed on your CV (such as that shown in Example 4 on page 60), there is no need to give the full addresses of your employers – in many cases just the company name will do. Where the nature of a company's business activities is adequately conveyed in the company name (e.g. Shoeland Shoe Shop), to elaborate further would be a waste of space and reading time.

Job descriptions

Highlight the main duties and responsibilities of each job, and emphasise any notable achievements. Give your job title, and be honest! If you feel that additional emphasis can be given to the weight of responsibility that you carry, give the job title of the person to whom you are/were responsible. Sometimes, senior company officials will be so well respected within an industry that the mere mention of their names commands attention, in which case you should include the names of your superiors, as in Example 6 on page 64.

Achievements

Many people (particularly those working in a sales environment) like to single out particular achievements in their different jobs, as in Example 6 on page 64. This inclusion will, of course, depend on the kind of jobs you have had, and the kind for which you are applying.

Industrial work placements

Industrial placements or university/college placements, whatever their duration, should be treated as a normal job in the career history, with the fact clearly stated in each case, as in Example 7 on page 65. If the placement was part of a qualification obtained some years ago, it may not be necessary to include the industrial placements, on account of the work experience now gained.

Part-time work

Many people work as a full-time employee for one organisation and, in their spare time, as a part-time employee for one, or several, other employers. If the part-time experience is directly relevant to the kind of work being sought, it could be dealt with immediately below the full-time career history, which will be set out in the usual way. After this, will appear:

Part-Time Work Experience

As always, this should run in reverse order.

But beware. Unless the part-time work in question is of special importance, you should think hard before including it. The prospective employer might decide that, if you continued with part-time work after joining him, your attention would be divided between the two jobs. This would certainly deter him, even if his fears were unjustified.

Many young people may feel hesitant in admitting to their part-time job as a supermarket shelf-stacker, or their summer job as a chicken-plucker, particularly when they are in the final year of a degree course applying for a more intellectually-challenging position. The choice is, as ever, yours and yours alone; however, the inclusion of such jobs does show a positive willingness to tackle almost anything. This personal quality is always an asset. Try to present the skills gained in these temporary jobs in a way that will help your application for your permanent job (see Example 1 on page 55 and Example 3 on page 59).

When a full-time career has been established, it is likely to overshadow anything that has gone before. Some part-time work may still be worth including, e.g. Territorial

Army weekend service. This would come under Outside Activities (see page 71), as would voluntary work in aid of charity, or perhaps the St John Ambulance Brigade.

What *not* to include

Reason for leaving

There is no need to give your reason for leaving any place of employment. It is generally accepted that it is unlikely the whole truth will always be told, especially in the case of the applicant who has given his employer a black eye! It is more effective to leave the reader with the impression that each job was superior to the previous one, even if this is not always quite the case.

Salary/wage details

As a rule, you should not put your salary expectations on a CV designed for general use – you may sell yourself short if applying for a job which would offer a larger salary. If a job application *asks* for details of your current salary, add this to your covering letter or accompanying e-mail (see page 112).

If you are submitting your CV to an online CV bank, you may wish to add your desired salary as this is one of the 'search agents' which recruiters may use to find suitable applicants for their positions. Try to be realistic – have a look at the salaries being offered for the kind of job you'd like, and consider your own experience and level of education in relation to these.

Common Problems

Pursuing more than one career?

Many people pursue two (or more) distinctly different careers. Often this situation arises when a preferred occupation is either highly over-subscribed or not adequately financially rewarding, so necessitating an alternative career in order to 'make ends meet'. One solution to this problem is to do a separate CV for each occupation, but this will leave you with huge unexplained time gaps, leaving potential employers wondering what you have been up to during this time. My advice is to write two differently-focused CVs, each bringing only one of the occupations to the fore. For example, if you have spent some time as a Chauffeur and some time as an Accountant, you might, when applying for another accounting position, go into full details about your accounting jobs, merely mentioning the dates and addresses for your Chauffeur jobs. This way the recruiter reading your CV should gain the impression that accounting is your primary occupation, your driving work merely something that has filled some time in between jobs. When applying for Chauffeur work, the emphasis will also be appropriately altered.

Filling out an application form?

Sometimes, when applying for jobs, you may be asked to complete an application form with more or less the same information as is contained on your CV. You may be tempted to attach a copy of your CV to the application form and write on it 'See enclosed CV' – DON'T! While a properly prepared CV can be expected to provide two-thirds to three-quarters of the information required on most application forms, there will still be other questions, often very important ones, which must be answered. Large organisations might distribute hundreds of returned application forms between several senior executives, with instructions to compile a list for the first interview. Suppose that, say, question 10 is the important one. Visualise the difficulty if applicants have answered it by advising scrutiny of the attached CV. For this reason, you are best advised to fill out the form in its entirety.

All questions relating to personal details, education, qualifications and training should be answered in the usual way (although it will often mean writing down again details which are already in your CV). Then read through the form carefully and answer any questions which are not catered for by the CV. Where the career history or employment experience is concerned, the form may have only a relatively small area in which to insert the briefest of details; in which case, that is what must be done. However, when the form concludes with one, two or even more blank pages for details of previous employment, it is common practice to write 'See enclosed CV' – and attach a copy.

5

EXAMPLE CAREER HISTORIES

The following examples should help to clarify what information the Career History section of your CV should contain.

Example 1 – A Student
Example 2 – A Licensee
Example 3 – A Computer Programmer
Example 4 – An Electrician seeking work offshore
Example 5 – A Motor Mechanic, newly discharged from HM Armed Forces and seeking work in civilian life.
Example 6 – An Estate Agent
Example 7 – An HND Work Placement
Example 8 – A Self-employed Building Contractor

Example 1 – A Student

PART-TIME WORK EXPERIENCE

(year) – (year) **Smith's Newsagents.**
22 Manor Road, Anytown,
Midshire.
– Morning newspaper round.

(Year) (Holidays) **Anytown Leisure Ltd.**
Promenade, Anytown,
Midshire.
– Cashier, handing out change to customers.

(Year) (Weekends) **Dot's Cake Shop.**
14 Belgrave Road,
Anytown, Midshire.
– Sales Assistant, selling bread and cakes, as well as helping in the bakery.

(Year) (Holidays) **Anytown Stables.**
Church Road, Anytown,
Midshire.
– Stable Yard Assistant, cleaning out stables, grooming and exercising horses.

Example 2 – A Licensee

EXPERIENCE/ACHIEVEMENTS

Feb (year) to present – The Plough Hotel (Brewman's Brewery), Foxglove Road, Anytown, Midshire.

– 28 bedrooms (en suite), 2 licensed bars, À la carte restaurant (80 covers), Functions room.

Licensed Manager responsible to the Area Manager for the day-to-day running of the business, including the recruitment, training and control of staff (32); organising weddings, parties, business conferences and Rotary functions for up to 120.

Achievement: Through improving public relations, making staff changes and applying tighter controls in all areas, a 15% increase in profitability was recorded in the first full year. This has been maintained.

June (year) to Feb. (year) – The Ship Tavern (Frothman's Brewery), Beach Road, Anytown, Midshire.

– 3 licensed bars, Dining-room with fast-food and full meals services (60 covers).

Licensed Manager responsible to the District Sales Manager for running the operation, including book-keeping, control of stock and cash and recruitment and training of staff (28). Catered for weddings, funerals, birthday parties and charity functions for up to 100.

EXPERIENCE/ACHIEVEMENTS Cont.

Mar. (year) to June (year) – The White Lady Bars and Leisure Complex, The Promenade, Anytown.

Bar Manager responsible for running this busy, sea-front, multi-bar operation.

Public Bar: Up to 300 customers, demanding a rapid flow of alcoholic and soft drinks, as well as bar snacks.

Lounge Bar: Customers comprised a mixed concentration of locals and holiday makers.

Cocktail Bar: Heavy lunch-time and late evening trade, from professional and business people.

Responsible for stock control and acquisition. Thirty-four full and part-time bar staff and cleaners.

Apr. (year) to Mar (year) – The Manor Grill-Room Restaurant, Olde Road, Anytown, Midshire.

– 75 covers, 1 licensed bar.

Assistant Manager responsible for helping the Manager to achieve his objectives, and deputising in his absence. Twenty-two full and part-time staff.

Aug. (year) to Apr. (year) – The Dog and Duck Inn, Orchard Lane, Anytown, Midshire.

– Public House (3 bars).

Bartender, serving beers, shorts and cocktails to customers from all levels of society.

EXPERIENCE/ACHIEVEMENTS Cont.

May (year) to Aug. (year) – Unemployed.

Nov. (year) to May (year) – The Black Owl (Mountain Brewery), Anytown, Midshire.

– Fully licensed residential hotel, 55 bedrooms.

Commis Chef – veg, larder and sweet.

Nov. (year) to Nov. (year) – The Olde Hall Inn (Free House), Hall Lane, Anytown, Midshire.

Trainee Cellarman.

July (year) to Nov. (year) – Anytown Box Co Ltd., Shore Road, Anytown, Midshire.

Trainee Box Maker.

Example 3 – A Computer Programmer

EXPERIENCE

Any.com July (year) – to date
Anytown Industrial Estate, Anytown, Midshire

Web Developer. Duties include redesigning, maintaining, uploading and creating new pages using HTML and Flash on www.any.com

Another.com Jan. (year) – July (year)
58 High Street, Anytown, Midshire

Web Designer. I designed and planned a website for commercial use. My duties included creating concepts, planning and adding pages, finding links, uploading and checking site using HTML and Java. I also dealt with artwork creation in Adobe Photoshop and integrating banner advertising on www.another.com

Some.com Aug. (year) – Jan. (year)
The Barkley Building, Anytown, Midshire

Web Design Assistant. Responsible to the Web Master. My duties included checking hyperlinks, using the Internet to research competitors and products and turning copywriter's text into HTML pages.

Spark's PC Store Feb. (year) – Aug. (year)
Anytown Shopping Centre, Midshire

Part-time Sales Assistant (week-ends and University holidays). My duties included explaining and demonstrating new hardware and software to customers and setting up display PCs.

Example 4 – An Electrician seeking work offshore

EXPERIENCE

June (year) – to date
Anytown Management Services Ltd

– Contracting to Cann Oil
Approved Electrician on Cann 'B' Platform – installation of electrical fire and gas systems.

May (year) – June (year)
Broadvale Engineering, Anytown

Approved Electrician on Morecambe Bay hook-up – installation and commissioning of fire and gas instrumentation; running and terminating cables; wiring PA systems; ladder racking and tray work.

Feb. (year) – May (year)
RCN Electrical Contractors

– Midchester Leisure Centre
Approved Electrician – installation of heavy gauge cable trunking.

Nov. (year) – Feb. (year)
AMA Nuclear Systems Plc

– Norsham Power Station
Approved Electrician – installation and testing of thermo-couples, strain gauges and microphones.

EXPERIENCE Continued

Mar. (year) – Nov. (year)
Hall & Rowe Ltd, Anytown

– New hypermarket for C & J
Approved Electrician – installation of EPOS computer systems, emergency lighting, via contactor controls; automatic doors; zone fire alarm systems; steel wire armoured cable.

Sept. (year) – Mar. (year)
BDR Construction (UK) Ltd

– Saudi Arabian Hospital Building Contract
Approved Electrician – installation of floor trunking and sockets; all theatre electrification; fire alarms; smoke and gas detection equipment.

June (year) – Sept. (year)
T & G Electric (Anytown) Ltd

June (year) – September (year)
Electrician/Approved Electrician.

June (year) – June (year)
Apprentice Electrician (Indentured).

Example 5 – A Motor Mechanic, newly discharged from HM Armed Forces and seeking work in civilian life.

EXPERIENCE

Oct. (year) to May (year) – Army
Royal Electrical and Mechanical Engineers.

July (year) – May (year)
Section Commander (UK) responsible for acquisition, control and inspection of all high and low cost items used in the repair and maintenance of tracked military vehicles. Twenty subordinate fitters and technicians.

April (year) – July (year)
Section Commander (Germany) – inspection and testing of wheeled military vehicles and the control and inspection of workshop equipment.

June (year) – April (year)
Corporal Mechanic (UN Forces – Cyprus) – control and acquisition of vehicle and equipment spare parts. Up to five subordinates.

October (year) – June (year)
Mechanic working in the UK and Germany, carrying out major repairs to heavy plant. Much of this work was done in field conditions, where inaccessibility demanded frequent improvisation.

Certificate of Service reads: Conduct Exemplary.
Rank on Discharge: Corporal.

Sept. (year) to Oct. (year)
Bardale Auto Services Ltd., Anytown, Midshire

Apprentice Motor Mechanic – full-time in the workshop while awaiting REME service.

Service in the Armed Forces will sometimes have been so involved that attempting to break it down into a conventional presentation would be impracticable. In such cases, a short narrative can be the best approach. For example:

EXPERIENCE

Oct. (year) to May (year) – Army
Royal Electrical and Mechanical Engineers.

After twelve months at the REME School of Mechanical Engineering, I had a variety of postings in the UK and Germany involving the servicing and repair of heavy plant. Then followed a three year period as a Corporal Mechanic, serving with the UN Forces in Cyprus, in control of vehicle and parts acquisition.

I became a Section Commander in (year), with responsibility for the inspection and testing of wheeled military vehicles, and for the control and inspection of workshop equipment.

On returning to the UK in (year), the number of subordinate personnel increased from five to twenty. My additional responsibilities included the control and inspection of a wide variety of high and low cost items, as well as the repair, maintenance and testing of wheeled and tracked vehicles.

Certificate of Service reads: Conduct Exemplary.

Rank on Discharge: Corporal.

Example 6 – An Estate Agent

EXPERIENCE/ACHIEVEMENTS

Feb. (year) to date – Anytown Estates Ltd.
105 – 107 High Street, Anytown, Midshire
– Estate Agents and Valuers (5 Branches)

September (year) – to date
Branch Manager (Hightown Branch) responsible to the Financial Director, Mr James Short, for the day-to-day running of the branch, with its high volume Midchester Building Society agency.

Duties include valuing domestic properties and securing new business; formulating press advertisements and property sales hand-outs; negotiating sales; liaising with solicitors; attending weekly management meetings; on-the-job staff training; interviewing and appointing branch staff (3).

ACHIEVEMENT: Exceeded (year) business target by 9.3%, while fees remained at 2% (firm).

February (year) – September (year)
Valuer/Negotiator (Anytown Branch) – valuing properties; formulating hand-outs; negotiating sales; liaising with solicitors; resolving problems. Assisted with staff recruitment and deputised in the Manager's absence.

ACHIEVEMENT: Won a weekend for two in Paris in (year) for the most improved performance at any of the five branches.

EXPERIENCE/ACHIEVEMENTS Cont.

Apr. (year) to Feb. (year) – Clock Publishing Ltd.
41 Cheapside, Anytown, Midshire
– Media publishers

Sales Agent – selling advertising space on Estate Agents' folders to tradesmen and retailers.

Example 7 – An HND Work Placement

EXPERIENCE

June (year) to Sept. (year) – The George Hotel
125 South Promenade, Anytown, Midshire

– Fully licensed residential hotel (45 en suite bedrooms)

Management Trainee on industrial placement. Receptionist – receiving guests; handling telephone enquiries; operating a computerised reservations and accounts system.

Example 8 – A Self-Employed Building Contractor

EXPERIENCE

Aug (year) to present – J Smith (Building contractor) Lower Lane, Anytown, Midshire

– New House Building; Extensions; Home Improvements etc.

Proprietor – totally responsible for running the business with up to six skilled tradesmen and ten labourers. Working an average of sixty-five hours a week, responsibilities include: purchasing materials; staff recruitment, motivation and control; preparation of tenders; book-keeping and VAT returns; liaising with all associated professions. Four contracts, each exceeding £70,000 in value, have been successfully completed in the last three years.

6

ADDITIONAL DETAILS

By now it should be very clear that whatever you add to your CV will depend on your individual circumstances. The following are some common additions, which can be added before or after the Career History section, as appropriate. Similar sub-headings may also appear on recruitment websites' online forms, so even if you don't want to add them all to your 'real' CV, it may be an idea to think about what you should write for each of them, should the need arise.

Profile

The Profile is designed to catch the reader's eye a few seconds after he has taken the CV from the envelope, or opened his e-mail attachment. The purpose of this inclusion is to give him a brief 'preview' of the applicant, in the hope that he will then be encouraged to read on. This is also the place to state your career aspirations, if these are not already obvious from the rest of the CV (if you have not already stated your Occupation, for example). The Profile usually appears after your Personal Details, and before your Education or Experience details.

If you intend to upload your CV to an online CV Bank, or to complete a website's CV form, remember that, in many cases, the 'Profile' section of your CV will be the first, and perhaps only, part of your details potential recruiters will see when searching for candidates, so it is worth paying special attention to this section's impact.

One of the dangers of an applicant's attempts to write a Profile is that the end result will be a description which impresses him far more than it will the reader. Many profiles are marred by overuse of cliché or stock phrases which are often meaningless, or inaccurate, in their description of the applicant. Try to avoid phrases like 'able to work on own initiative and as part of a team' or 'enthusiastic and self-motivated individual' unless these *honestly* describe you. Another problem is that a Profile takes up valuable space and must not therefore be too long. As with all other aspects of CV preparation, brevity is the watchword.

Example Profile:

PROFILE
Management Accountant with the ability to implement administrative and financial management controls. Extensive knowledge of computer software packages, including Microsoft Excel and Lotus 1-2-3.

Experience in Brief

With some trades and professions, a brief Summary of Experience and/or skills acquired is more appropriate than a simple Profile. For example, a motor mechanic with a wide range of experience might offer the following bullet points:

Example Experience in Brief:

EXPERIENCE IN BRIEF

- Electronic Ignition Systems.
- Electronic Fuel Injection.
- Direct Fuel Injection (Diesel).
- Use of diagnostic equipment.
- Heavy and light vehicle transmissions (automatic and manual).
- Maintenance and testing of heavy plant, i.e. Caterpillar 992 and 988 Wheeled Shovels; Catapillar 773 and 777 Dump Trucks.

Core Skills/Summary of Skills

This is similar, although not the same, as the Experience in Brief, and so I would advise that you do not use both. Candidates within many industries, particularly IT, may find it useful to provide a bullet point summary of their main skills, before giving fuller details in the Education and Career History sections of the CV. (This is a very common sub-heading in online CV forms.) Such skills often involve the use of computer software packages and platforms or programming languages, in which case you should list the skills in order of proficiency (your strongest first), perhaps with an honest rating of your ability by the side of each entry. These skills may also include typing speed in words per minute (wpm), shorthand (again, with your speed in wpm), any foreign languages you speak (if you haven't already added these under a separate sub-heading), as well as more general qualities such as a good telephone manner or accurate spelling and grammar.

Example of a General Skills Summary:

SUMMARY OF SKILLS:

Computer Skills:
Word (working knowledge), Excel (working knowledge), Outlook (working knowledge), Internet Explorer (working knowledge), PowerPoint (beginner)

Languages:
French (fluent spoken, school level written) and German (school level spoken and written)

Office Skills:
Typing speed 70 wpm, shorthand speed 110 wpm, excellent telephone manner and customer facing skills.

Example of an IT Core Skills Summary:

CORE SKILLS:

- Unix Administration (Solaris/Linux/OpenBSD)
- NT Administration (NT4/Win2K)
- NT/Unix Integration (SAMBA/Kerberos)
- Server Administration (RAID server/Solstice Disksuite/Clustering)
- Network Administration (FDDI/TCP-IP/ Firewalls/Packet Filtering/DNS admin)
- Programming – High Level (C++/C/Java/ JavaScript/Pascal/ Lisp)
- Web Design (HTML/XHTML/XML/XSL/PerlASP/ JSP)
- Databases (SQL/Web Integration)

Outside Activities or Hobbies

Although some of my clients prefer not to use valuable space on items such as outside activities, these can offer an employer a picture of you as a rounded, interesting individual. The kind of pursuits you get up to outside office hours will play a large part in forming your personality and attitude to work. At interviews you may find that a discussion of your outside activities will take place, partly as ice-breaking conversation, but mostly as a means of discovering what really interests and stimulates you. People who appear to be solely driven by their work and career aspirations may well make hard-working employees, but they are also boring to spend time with. Remember that your application may well be judged as much by your personality as by your qualifications and practical experience. If you are lacking in the latter two, make the former sound as interesting as possible!

If you are keen on sports or keep-fit, mention this as you may increase your chances of a successful application by showing that you are a fit and healthy person. Additionally, involvement in a team sport, such as rugby or netball, shows co-operation skills and a sense of 'team spirit' – qualities which many recruiters look for in potential employees. Any voluntary work for charity you may have carried out will show your compassionate side, as well as showing that you are not afraid of a little hard work. Reading, visiting the cinema, travelling abroad, evening classes, playing a musical instrument, cooking, amateur dramatics, tinkering with the car, camping, caring for pets, home computing and so on are all worthwhile inclusions to this section.

If your only regular leisure pursuit is propping up the bar at your local pub, then you may want to include 'socialising' as an outside interest, but do try to think of a couple of others to put before it – nobody wants to employ a drunkard! (In the case of young applicants, the recruiter may find it somewhat suspicious if you do not mention your social activities – very few students spend all of their time studying!)

As with all parts of your CV, honesty is always the best policy – although many people mistakenly think of themselves as good 'actors', few can manage to carry off a lie convincingly. If you claim to be a qualified parachuting instructor, when in reality you suffer vertigo changing a lightbulb, you do not want to take the risk of having your bluff called!

Example Outside Activities:

OUTSIDE ACTIVITIES:
Five-a-side football, reading Science Fiction novels and acting as a voluntary coach driver for the Anytown Association for Disabled Children.

Languages

If you have learned a foreign language, say so! The ability to read or, even better, speak in a foreign language is beneficial in many jobs. Your CV should show the level of your fluency (whether you are bilingual, fluent, school-level, beginning to learn the language, or some other level), and whether this applies to speaking, reading or both. If your only use of a foreign language is when you ordered a beer and a paella on holiday in Tenerife last summer, do not exaggerate your level of fluency – as before, you cannot take the risk of getting caught out.

Example Foreign Languages listing:

LANGUAGES:

Bengali – Bilingual
German – School-level (Spoken and Written)
French – School-level (Spoken)

Achievements at School/College/University

Positions held at school can sometimes influence the reader's attitude, especially when the post requires self-motivation and the ability to shoulder heavy responsibility. To have been a school prefect is an indicator pointing in the right direction. A House Captain or Captain of a school team, e.g. football, cricket, athletics, netball, etc., indicates a degree of leadership ability. To have been a member of a school team suggests an ability to function in harmony with others.

Positions held at university are worthwhile inclusions, provided they do not appear so time-consuming that the reader might gain the impression that you have your priorities in the wrong order. It is probably not a good idea to mention your position of chairman of the Student Union Excessive Beer Drinking Society, proud of this achievement as you may be!

List your achievements after the details of your academic qualifications.

ple of School/University Achievements' listing:

ACHIEVEMENTS:

School:	Head Girl in (year) Captain of Netball Team and member of Hockey Team. Duke of Edinburgh Award Scheme – Silver Award
University:	Treasurer of the Anytown University Student Union in (year). Pictures Editor for the University Newspaper in (year).

Career Objective/s

If you have not already stated your Occupation in the Personal Details section of your CV, and if it is not very clear from your Career History just what kind of job you want, you may wish to add a brief section stating your Career Objective or Objectives. This is particularly relevant to CVs being published on or uploaded to the Web, where recruiters from many industries and professions may be looking at your CV, especially if your career history spans several different career paths.

Example Career Objective:

CAREER OBJECTIVE:

Looking to further my career within the New Media and Marketing industries.

References

Most recruiters will, at some point, ask for some sort of reference from a trustworthy individual who knows you on a personal or professional basis. You may wish to state at the end of your CV that you have references available – do not waste space supplying the referees' names and addresses just yet. A minority of people possess written testimonials from previous employers. Where these are outstanding in their praise of an individual's integrity and competence, I usually recommend enclosing the best two, whatever the person's trade or profession might be.

It is usual for one of your references to be from your current employer and, although it is a generally accepted rule of courtesy not to contact the employer without the applicant's permission, you may not want to risk word getting around that you are looking for a new job. You may ask a friend or colleague (but not a partner or member of your family) to act as a referee, but be careful who you pick. A reference from an old friend who works as a Bank Manager is likely to carry far more weight than one from your local pub's Landlord!

Example Reference citing:

REFERENCES:
The names and addresses of two referees are available on request.

7

COMPLETE CVS

On the following pages are eleven complete CVs which should give you an overall picture of how everything fits together. As you will see, in each case different decisions have been made as to the inclusion or exclusion of the various subheadings – you will have to make these decisions for yourself based on your own education, experience and the industry and type of job to which you aspire.

In each case, the CVs are laid out in accordance with the kind of role being applied for. These are intended as a broad guide – your CV will look much more thought-out and unique if you design your own layout, rather than slavishly copying those featured here. Refer back to Chapter 1 for further guidance on presentation.

Example 1 – A Retail Manager

Rashid Ahmed

Address:	8 Ashburton Close, Anytown, Midshire, XX1 1YY
Home Tel:	01888 888888
Mobile Tel:	07888 888888
E-mail:	ahmed@anymail.com
Gender:	Male
Date of Birth:	19th July (year). Age (XX)
Place of Birth:	Anytown, Midshire
Nationality:	British
Marital Status:	Living with partner, no children.
Driving Licence:	Current (clean). Have own car.

CURRICULUM VITAE

Profile

High achieving Retail Manager able to exceed budgets consistently, despite strong local competition. Regularly in the top five of the Company's 372 retail outlets.

Experience/Achievements

Oct. (year) to present – Fashionwear Shops Plc
121 – 129 Arcadia Road, Anytown, Midshire

January (year) to present
General Manager (Midchester) responsible to the Area Manager for meeting sales budgets and controlling the expenditure budget to set parameters.

1

Rashid Ahmed

Experience/Achievements Cont.

Duties include conducting weekly staff meetings; attending monthly management meetings; cost control (including cleaning and maintenance); presentation and display; stock control; ensuring compliance with Health and Safety regulations.

Achievement: 12% increase in business turnover in first full financial year.

October (year) to January (year)
Assistant Manager (Northend) responsible for the training and motivation of sales staff (10) using EPOS; completing staff time-sheets and appraisals; stock control; security of cash and premises (key holder); presentation and display.

Nov. (year) to Oct. (year) – Kelly & Smart Ladies' Fashions
71– 75 Burlington Road, Anytown, Midshire

Manager (Anytown) responsible to the Financial Director for the day-to-day running of the business. Duties included recruitment and training of staff (5); designing window and interior displays; formulating and placing local advertisements; balancing daily takings; banking; submitting a weekly trading analysis; security (key holder).

2

Rashid Ahmed

Experience/Achievements Cont.

Achievement: Consistently exceeded agreed budgets, despite a strong presence from three similar retail shops within a distance of three hundred metres.

Education and Qualifications

Sept. (year) to July (year) – St George's High School, Anytown, Midshire

June (year) – 2 'A' Levels (Grades B and D)
June (year) – 9 GCSEs (Grades A – C)

Training

Fashionwear Shops Plc

Feb. (year)	Training the Trainer (1 week)
July (year)	Man Management/Leadership (2 days)
May (year)	Computerised Stock Control (2 days)
Oct. (year)	Motivating the Customer (1 day)

References
Available on request.

Example 2 – A Regional Sales Manager

James McDougall BA
14 Park Drive, Anytown, Midshire, XX1 3HH

Home Tel: 01888 555555
Mobile Tel: 07666 333333
E-Mail: jmcd@anymail.com
Web: www.jmcd.anymail.com
DOB: 5th October (year)
Marital Status: Single
Occupation: Sales Manager

Profile:
An adaptable candidate offering the benefit of 15 years' successful sales experience.

Experience:
Flakey Friend Ltd *April (year) to present*
126-132 Elephants Walk, Anytown, Midshire
– Manufacturers and Distributors of Breakfast Cereals

August (year) to present
Midland Counties Regional Sales Manager responsible to the National Sales Manager, Mr J Jones, for the profitable growth of business throughout the region. Responsibilities cover promotions, distribution and the effective display of products; recruitment and development of sales representatives (8).

During this time, a 27% increase in sales (volume) was achieved and sales targets are consistently being exceeded by 3%-5%.

1

James McDougall BA

Experience cont:

March (year) to August (year)
Area Sales Manager responsible to the Regional Sales Manager for effective space allocation and promotion of the company's products. Six subordinate representatives.

Consistently exceeded sales targets, by up to 6%.

April (year) – March (year)
Sales Representative – developing new business throughout the area, and promoting a new product.

Awarded an engraved gold watch, presented by the Managing Director in person, in recognition of the success with which the new product had been launched in the area.

Wispy Hair Products Ltd *June (year) to April (year)*
New Road, Anytown, Midshire
Sales Representative – developing the company's business through High Street outlets and supermarket chains.

The Southern Gas Co *February (year) to June (year)*
Leigh Road, Anytown, Midshire
Showroom Sales Assistant – selling domestic gas appliances.

2

James McDougall BA

Experience cont:

Anytown Colourings Ltd *July (year) to Feb. (year)*
Lowe Road, Anytown, Midshire
– Suppliers of Paint and Wall coverings to the Decorating Trade.

Warehouse Assistant – unloading and stacking incoming stock.

Training:

Professional Salesmanship October (year) – 3 days
Effective Presentations June (year) – 1 day

Education:

University of Northshire *September (year) – June (year)*
BA Hons (2:ii) History

Anytown High School *September (year) to June (year)*
June (year) – 2 'A' Levels (English and Maths)
June (year) – 5 GCE 'O' Levels

Outside Interests:

In my spare time I enjoy reading, socialising and mountain biking: I recently raised £500 for Anytown Dogs' Home on a 300 mile bike ride.

3

Example 3 – A Financial Consultant

Samantha Goldstein

Personal Details

Address:	131 The Drive, Anytown, Midshire, XX2 3GG
Telephone:	01888 000111 (Evenings) 07333 333333 (Mobile)
E-mail:	sam@anymail.com
D.O.B.:	2nd January (year)
Marital Status:	Married with 1 daughter (aged 10)

Profile

An experienced Financial Consultant seeking to further her career in a larger financial corporation. Computer literate and with personable client-facing manner.

Career History

Anytown Financial Services Ltd *Nov. (year) to present*
London Street, Anytown, Midshire

- Financial Consultant visiting potential clients, identifying client needs and advising on life assurance, pensions and investments.
- *Achievement:* Expanded the client base by 57% in the first year.

Eternal Life Assurance Ltd *Feb. (year) to Nov. (year)*
78 – 82 High Street, Anytown, Midshire

- Area Representative (Hightown) responsible for selling life assurance, personal pensions, company pension plans, investment packages and endowment mortgages.

1

Samantha Goldstein

Career History Continued

K E Tagg Associates *Aug. (year) – Feb. (year)*
21 Leicester Road, Anytown, Midshire
– Insurance Brokers

- Client Adviser – dealing with all aspects of property and motor insurance, i.e. supplying quotations; amending policies; processing claims; updating files; preparing accounts.

Highgate Developments Ltd. *Apr. (year) – Aug. (year)*
Greenacres Road, Anytown, Midshire
– House Builders

- Sales Negotiator – conducting show house viewings; advising on fixtures and fittings; selling sites; liaising with site agent, company's solicitor and vendor's solicitor.

Anytown Estates *July (year) to Apr. (year)*
105 – 107 High Street

- Clerk/Receptionist

Education

University of Greentown *Sept. (year) to June (year)*
BA Business Studies (2.ii)

Anytown College *Sept. (year) to June (year)*
June (year) 'A' levels in Economics, Maths, Further Maths and General Studies (grades A – B)

Anytown Grammar School *Sept. (year) to June (year)*
June (year) 9 GCSEs (grades A – C), including English and Maths

2

Samantha Goldstein

IT Skills
Working use of Word, Excel, Oracle, PowerPoint, Outlook and Internet Explorer.

Hobbies
Cookery and Amateur Dramatics. I am currently learning to speak Russian at evening classes at Anytown Community Centre.

References
I shall happily provide two references on request.

3

Example 4 – A Managing Director

Michael Wallis

PERSONAL DETAILS

Address: 469 Long Drive, Anytown, Midshire, XX4 5TT
Tel: 01888 555555
Fax: 01888 555444
E-mail: mike@anymail.com
Age: XX
Marital Status: Single
Passport No: X 777777 Y
Driving Licence: Current (full). Have own transport.
Preferred Location: Prepared to work anywhere in Europe.

CAREER HISTORY

Baldwin Barker & Co Ltd **March (year) to present**
86 Tower Gate, Anytown, Midshire
– Property Investment and Development

July (year) to present
Managing Director responsible to the Chairman for instant decision making and the day-to-day running of the company: liaising with company Architects, Planning Consultants, Solicitors, Accountants and Bankers in the planning and execution of developments, up to £4.5 million. Responsibilities include scrutinising main contractors' returned tender documents and presiding at high-level meetings. Regular liaison with co-directors covering sales, purchases and leases.

1/4

Michael Wallis

CAREER HISTORY Cont

Achievement:
Through encouraging an improved performance from existing staff members and recruiting highly motivated executives of proven ability, company turnover increased by 35% within two years. Despite adverse market forces, the level of activity has been maintained with corresponding profitability. Recently rewarded by the company with a Porsche.

September (year) to July (year)
Director of Purchasing and Development responsible to the Managing Director for researching proposed development and redevelopment projects, i.e. ensuring cost-effectiveness, long-term viability, or quick resale profit potential; obtaining engineers' soil test reports; negotiating the purchase of green field sites and existing buildings, e.g. office blocks, factories and warehouses; liaising with all relevant professions.

March (year) to September (year)
Buyer/Negotiator responsible for travelling throughout the UK, negotiating options on agricultural land, as well as purchasing land with outline planning permission. Required to liaise with Architects and chief Planning Officers, and participate in the presentation of planning applications. Fought and won an appeal to the DOE over the refusal of planning permission to build a new office block. Four subordinate head office personnel.

2/4

Michael Wallis

CAREER HISTORY Cont

Midshire Estates Ltd **Feb. (year) to Mar. (year)**
122 – 124 Clifton Road, Anytown, Midshire
– Estate Agents, Auctioneers and Valuers (30 branches)

Branch Manager responsible to the Managing Director for the efficient day-to-day running of the branch, i.e. securing instructions to sell houses, preparing valuations, newspaper advertisements and property fact sheets; negotiating sales; advising purchasers with regard to mortgage facilities.

EDUCATION

September (year) – June (year)
Anytown University, Anytown, Midshire
BSc Economics (1st)

September (year) – June (year)
Anytown High School, Anytown, Midshire
June (year) – 'A' Levels in Maths (A), Economics (A) and Politics (A)
June (year) – 11 GCSEs (9 As, 2 Bs)

TRAINING
Anytown Business Training Centre
August (year) – Man Management (12 weeks)
February (year) – Executive Marketing (3 days)
January to April (year) – Japanese for Business

3/4

Michael Wallis

LANGUAGES

French – fluent spoken and written
German – fluent spoken and written
Japanese – business level spoken

OUTSIDE INTERESTS

Watersports, walking in the countryside with my dogs and tap dancing.

REFERENCES

Available on request

4/4

Example 5 – A Teacher

Personal Details:

Name: CAROLINE BAKER BSc (Hons) MA (Ed)

Address: 31 Leafy Lane, Anytown, Midshire, XX3 9HH
Tel: 01888 222222 (evenings only)
E-Mail: caroline.baker@anymail.com
Date of Birth: 14 August (year)
Nationality: British
Marital Status: Married, with daughter aged 13
Available: September (year)
Preferred Location: Within 50km (30 miles) of Anytown

Profile:
A hard-working teacher of both GCSE and 'A' level Mathematics to students of all ages and abilities, who aims to inspire students with her passion for Maths.

Employment History:

Anytown High School *September (year) to present*
Head of Mathematics
Made part of the senior teaching staff after 18 months' employment, with special responsibility for devising new strategies, policies and practices to be implemented by staff. Duties include co-ordinating internal and external examinations, acting as link between the Head and the rest of the staff, as well as day-to-day teaching of 'A' level to VI form groups, and GCSE and Key Stage 3 Maths to large, mixed-sex classes of varying ethnic background and ability (including special needs).

1

Employment History Cont.

Anytown Grammar School *Sept. (year) to July (year)*
Teacher of Mathematics
Teaching GCSE and 'A' level Maths, Pure Maths and Further Maths to small (15 to 20 pupils) classes of ability-streamed boys. Closely involved with timetabling during Deputy Head's maternity leave. Proposed the integration of a CD-ROM/Internet-based homework system for year 10 students, which was successfully applied.

Career break to raise child *April (year) to Sept. (year)*
I made use of this time spent at home with my child to write an easy-to-follow guide to basic mathematics (see overleaf).

Anytown Community College *Sept. (year) to July (year)*
Teacher of Mathematics
Second in the Mathematics Department, teaching GCSE Maths to mature students and young people who have been out of education for some time. My one-to-one approach and sensitive evaluation of students as individual cases helped achieve a 70% increase in the course pass rate over four years.

Education

Anytown Institute of Education *Sept. (year) to June (year)*
MA in Education

2

Education Cont.

University of Midshire *Sept.(year) to June (year)*
BSc in Mathematics (2:i)

Anytown Grammar School *Sept. (year) to June (year)*
June (year) – 4 'A' levels, June (year) – 9 'O' levels

Publications
Baker, Caroline. *Making Maths Fun.* (Anybooks: Westshire) (year).

IT Skills
Working use of various Wordprocessing, Spreadsheet and Database software.

Interests and Hobbies
Ballroom dancing, DIY and Home Computing.

References
Available on request.

3

Example 6 – A Joiner

Mark Harris – Professional Joiner

Address:	5 The Lanes, Anytown, Midshire, XX1 3TT
Home Tel:	01888 000000
Mobile Tel:	07888 000000
Home Fax:	01888 000111
Date of Birth:	19th March (year)
Marital Status:	Single
Nationality:	British/Australian

Profile

A versatile and creative worker with over 15 years' experience of Carpentry.

Experience

F Lynch & Son Ltd. February (year) to date
217 Beacon Road, Garth Industrial Estate, Anytown Midshire
– Builders, Shopfitters and Bar Fitters

Foreman Joiner on a £5m club refit and extension. Responsible for the supervision of 38 joiners, plumbers, electricians, bricklayers and labourers engaged in the construction of period bars, static and revolving stages, all backstage facilities and a restaurant.

JS Rigg (Builders) Ltd. October (year) to February (year)
45 Aqueduct Street, Anytown, Midshire

Foreman Joiner – supervision of twenty joiners on the rebuilding of a 300 bedroom, 4 star hotel, damaged by fire: bars; studdings; spiral staircases; hardwood dance floors; door casings.

1

Mark Harris - Professional Joiner

Experience Continued

HP Construction and Design Ltd. Nov. (year) to Oct. (year)
106 - 108 Victoria Road, Anytown, Midshire
- Public House and Hotel Refurbishment Contractors
Joiner in the workshop making bars, back fittings, door casings and mock period timber beams. Worked on site - fixing false ceilings and raised areas.

E F Wall & Sons Ltd. March (year) to Nov. (year)
81 - 83 Clay Street, Anytown, Midshire
- Building Contractors
Joiner - first, second and final fix on new houses.

Oak Tree Joinery Nov. (year) to Mar. (year)
28-30 Coronation Road, Anytown, Midshire
- Manufacturers of Replacement Doors and Windows
Bench Hand/Installer making and fitting uPVC windows and doors.

Joseph Yorke & Co Ltd July (year) to Nov. (year)
35 Oak Road, Anytown, Midshire
- Building Contractors

July (year) to November (year)
Joiner - first, second and final fix on an exclusive housing development

July (year) - July (year)
Apprentice Joiner (Indentured) - two years in the joinery shop; two years supervised on-the-job training.

Mark Harris - Professional Joiner

Education and Qualifications

Anytown College of Further Education
September (year) to June (year)
- Day release and evening classes
    June (year) - City and Guilds of London Institute
    Craft Certificate in Carpentry and Joinery

Anytown High School, Midshire
September (year) to June (year)
    June (year) CSE
        Woodwork (1)
        Art (1)
        Engineering Drawing (2)
        Mathematics (3)
        English (3)
        German (4)

Hobbies
Playing squash, family activities and reading.

References
Available on request.

3

Example 7 – A Nurse

Mary O'Connor

Address:	12 Portman Square, Anytown, Midshire, XX1 2YY
Home Tel:	01888 333333
Mobile Tel:	07888 333333
E-mail:	mary@anymail.com
D.O.B.:	7th August (year)
Marital Status:	Married, 3 children (aged 13, 15 and 21)
Nationality:	British
Occupation:	Senior Staff Nurse

Profile

A skilled Senior Nurse and leader of a multi-disciplinary team, providing a high standard of care to children and their families.

Employment History

St Joseph's Hospital Sept.(year) to date
Anytown, Midshire
Senior Staff Nurse (F grade) in a busy paediatric medical ward. Responsibilities include: managing the ward; caring for children following ENT, orthopaedic and general surgery; and holding bleeps.

East Midshire General June (year) to Sept. (year)
Anytown, Midshire
Staff Nurse on nights in a small paediatric unit of a General Hospital, managing the very specialised care of children with cardiac and respiratory illnesses.

1

Mary O'Connor

Employment History Cont.

St Mark's Hospital Nov.(year) to June (year)
Anytown, Midshire
Student Nurse (General). Caring for children, adults, expectant mothers and the elderly. Completed RGN training.

Greenacres Home July (year) to Nov. (year)
Anytown, Midshire
Nursing and Care Assistant providing respite care for children with learning and/or physical disabilities.

Education and Training

St Marks Hospital, Anytown Midshire
Sept. (year) Registered General Nurse

Anytown University, Anytown, Midshire
June (year) BA (Hons) Health Studies

Anytown Grammar School
June (year) 'A' Levels in Biology and English
June (year) 5 GCSEs, including Biology

Hobbies
Member of the Anytown Amateur Operatics Society and keen swimmer.

2

Example 8 – A Software Developer (An on-line CV)

Paul Snowforth

E-mail:	paul@anymail.com
Web:	www.snowforth.anymail.com
Date of Birth:	10th August (year)
Location:	Anytown, UK

Curriculum Vitae

Core Skills

- Programming in Perl, C, C++, Java (under Linux, Solaris and Open BSD)
- UNIX systems administration and mail servers (sendmail, qmail and exim), Apache, INN, DNS servers (BIND and djbdns), data bases (MySQL, Postgresql and Informix)
- I have also kept up with the development of HTML, Javascript, CSS and XML

Work History

Technical Solutions Ltd (year – present)
I am employed as a Developer by Technical Solutions Ltd, which builds on-line communities including Anymail and Anyshop, using the skills mentioned above on a daily basis. I am a Team Leader of a group of four Developers.

Page 1 of 3

Paul Snowforth

Work History

Cutting Edge Ltd (year – year)
I was employed as a Technical Consultant and Programmer, writing CGI scripts in Perl (5) and performing data base integration using Cold Fusion (1.5–3) to serve Microsoft Access data bases. Some work involved writing HTML and Javascript, graphics production (using Adobe Photoshop 5 and Illustrator 8), DHTML and Stylesheets.

BetaTech Ltd (year – year)
While studying for my MSc, I worked as a part-time Help Desk Technician, offering advice and assistance over the telephone to customers. This role required a wide range of trouble-shooting knowledge, spanning many software platforms and applications.

Education

Northtown University (year – year)
MSc in Computer Science (Distinction)

University of Anyborough (year – year)
BA (Hons) in *Literae Humaniores* (2:ii)

Anytown Grammar School (year – year)
June (year) – 3 'A' Levels (grade A)
June (year) – 8 GCSEs (grades A – C)

Page 2 of 3

Paul Snowforth

Other Interests

I enjoy writing code in my spare time, as well as at work, and am involved with the design and administration of a Multi-User Dungeon (a text-based, interactive, Internet-based, role-playing game), Elephant Mud. I also enjoy listening to all sorts of music, reading widely and spending time with friends.

Page 3 of 3

Example 9 – A Personal Assistant

Charlotte Higgins

Address:	45 Third Street, Anytown, Midshire XX3 3YY
Home Tel:	01888 888888
Mobile Tel:	07888 888888
E-mail:	Charlotte@anymail.com
Date of Birth:	19th January (year)
Marital Status:	Single, no children
Nationality:	British
Preferred Location:	Prepared to work anywhere in the world

Work History

Mullet Miggins & Co Ltd, Anytown Branch
Dec (year) to date
– Chartered and Public Accountancy
Secretary to three Tax Managers before becoming PA to one of the partners. My duties include: typing; invoicing; filing; post duties; stationery orders; keeping a diary; organising meetings; organising and running seminars.

Anytown Housing Association
June (year) to Dec (year)
Receptionist in a large and busy building. My duties included greeting officials and other visitors to the building; typing; filing; temporary PA to Finance Director during periods of absence and maternity leave.

1

Charlotte Higgins

Work History Continued

Midshire Building Contractors
Hogsback Road, Anytown, Midshire
Oct (year) to June (year)
Office/Accounts Assistant responsible for telephone bookings, taking payments by credit/debit cards, handling of cash and cheques, chasing debts and assisting purchase/bought ledger.

Boris and Berkin Trading Ltd
Trading Estate, Anytown, Midshire
Feb (year) to Oct (year)
My role as Secretary was to assist the Regional Sales and Marketing Director, 6 Sales Managers and additional support for 48 Sales Reps. Typing, invoicing, ordering goods, updating records and general administration.

Walsh Brothers Publishing
52 – 60 Acre Street, Anytown, Midshire
Mar (year) to Feb (year)
– Publishers of Business and Trade magazines
Receptionist/Secretary responsible for answering the phone, greeting customers and suppliers, as well as typing, filing and general administration.

2

Charlotte Higgins

Education and Qualifications

Anytown High School **(year) to (year)**
June (year) – 5 GCSEs, including English and Maths
April (year) – RSA Typing, Audio Typing and Word Processing Stages 1–3

Anytown College **May to August (year)**
Part-time summer course in Spoken French. Awarded certificate of merit.

Interests and Hobbies

Home computing, European travel and DIY.

3

Example 10 – An Advertising Executive

Gail T Clarkson

Address:	The Cottage, Bushy Road, Anytown, Midshire, XX1 1YY
Home Tel:	01888 888888
Mobile Tel:	07888 888888
E-mail:	gail@anymail.com
Web:	www.clarkson.anymail.com
D.O.B:	22nd April (year)
Marital Status:	Living with partner, two sons aged 12 and 13.

Profile

A self-confident, versatile Advertising Executive with extensive client contact experience.

Work History

AAA Advertising Dec (year) to present
Account Executive responsible for a portfolio of client accounts. My duties include drafting adverts, advising on appropriate media (including Internet and newspaper) and booking the ads. Promoted from Accounts Assistant to Account Executive within one year.

Achievements: Employee of the Month for three months this year.

1

Gail T Clarkson

Work History Cont.

Brown Media June (year) to Dec (year)
Accounts Assistant, reporting to the Chief Advertising Consultant, John Brown. I was involved with preparing and giving concept presentations to clients, including several major High Street banks. I also was responsible for writing and editing ad copy and liaising with artists and freelance writers, working to tight deadlines and budgets.

Achievements: Successfully bid for a contract with the Midshire Building Society, which went on to account for 15% of the company's revenue in (year). Was rewarded with a case of Bollinger champagne.

Glossy Publishing Oct (year) to June (year)
Trainee Accounts Assistant in a busy magazine publishing company. My duties involved selling commercial and classified advertising space in four major women's magazines, as well as participating in general office administration.

Achievements: Successfully completed in-house training and consistently exceeded sales targets by at least 10% each week.

2

Gail T Clarkson

Education

Anytown University
Oct (year) to June (year)
June (year) BA (Hons) Media Studies (2:ii)

Anytown Grammar School
Sept (year) to June (year)
June (year) 2 'A' levels (grade B)
June (year) 7 GCSEs (grades A to C)

Languages

French – school-level written and spoken
German – beginner spoken

Hobbies

Cooking and mountain bike riding. I am also taking an evening class at Anytown College in classical guitar.

3

Example 11 – The Wrong Way to Write Your Own CV

Michelle Brown

Personal Details:
Address: 85 New Road, Anytown, Midshire, XX1 1YY
Telephone: 01888 555333 Date of Birth: 28th March (year)
Marital Status: Living with partner
Children: Darren – born 6th July (year) and Sharon – born 2nd May (year)
Driving Licence: No

Education and Qualifications:
Anytown High School (5 years), Anytown College of Further Education (2 years).
Qualifications – 6 GCSE subjects and an RSA Wordprocessing Certificate

Work Experience:
With having to take care of my children, I have not had a full-time job since leaving college. Darren is now at school, and my mum looks after him during the holidays. Sharon has started at her nursery school and my boyfriend's mum takes her and picks her up, so I am now looking for a job.

I had a full-time job with Day, Knight & Co Chartered Accountants, 8 Water Street, Anytown, and went to college in the evenings. But I had to leave that job to have Darren.

I started work as an Office Junior. Then they advertised for a Typist/Receptionist. I applied and was given the position. I was more or less in charge of the office, until I left to have Darren.

Since Darren was born, I have worked three evenings a week as a Barmaid at the Dog and Partridge Inn, Ball Street, Anytown. I had two months off when Sharon was born, but they took me on again because they said I was so good at the job.

During my last year at school, I was a Shelf Stacker at Anytown Supermarket. This helped me to develop an understanding of the work ethic and enabled me to enhance my interpersonal skills.

Hobbies:
My hobbies are my children, playing video games and socialising.

So what is wrong with this CV? Just about everything! Let's look at it one section at a time.

Personal Details
These vital details appear to have been thrown at the paper, and then allowed to remain at the point of impact. The reader's eyes will be darting from side to side across the page, in a frantic search for information. The need to offer a presentation which is easy for the eye to scan down is clearly illustrated here. Equally important is the selective use of bold and italic text, which is non-existent in this example.

From a content point of view, Michelle has not stated whether that given is an evening or daytime telephone number – this will make it difficult for employers to get in touch with her in the unlikely event that they should want to interview her. She has also stated that she hasn't got a driving licence – there is no need to do this!

Education and Qualifications
If the reader proves sufficiently determined to arrive at this section, he will notice that there is no mention of starting or finishing dates for any of Michelle's schooling. As Michelle has no real qualifications other than her GCSEs, she would be best advised to include the subjects and grades achieved. Her education should be listed *after* her work experience, what there is of it . . .

Work Experience
Can you tell which was Michelle's most recent job? Well, since Sharon is the younger of the two children, and Sharon's birth is given as the reason for her temporary absence from the Dog and Partridge, I would say that the second job was her most recent. But don't think about it too long, or you will soon be as muddle-headed

as she! This confusion is caused by her failure to think about what she was doing beforehand, in order to get a clear outline plan of what she was trying to convey. Instead, she has simply spilled the contents of her mind onto the paper, resulting in a composition which tells us at least as much about Darren and Sharon as it does about her work.

Even more off-putting is the obviously high opinion she has of herself, *viz* ‘they took me on again because they said I was so good at the job’. When referring to her job change at Day, Knight & Co, she says, ‘I applied and I was given the position’, which gives an impression of smugness. She goes on to say, ‘I was more or less in charge of the office, until I left to have Darren’. Not only will vague statements of this kind fail to impress the reader, they will positively discourage him. Furthermore, in this instance he will have cause for serious doubts about the truth of what she is saying: no self-respecting firm of Chartered Accountants would put someone as seemingly disorganised and scatty as she in charge of a photocopier, let alone an office!

Further on, she says of her job at the supermarket, ‘This helped me to develop an understanding of the work ethic and enabled me to enhance my interpersonal skills’. I really do not believe that she has the remotest idea what she means here. She must have read it somewhere and thought it looked good. What it says to me is that her career has passed its peak, and that she should resign herself to another forty years at the Dog and Partridge.

Hobbies

Michelle has listed ‘socialising’ as one of her interests, which, in her case, is not a wise thing to do as her only other interest, besides her children, is playing video games. If I were reading this CV (had I bothered to read this far), I would guess that she probably spends an excessive amount of time on the other side of the bar at the Dog and Partridge. This is the wrong impression to give in a CV, since the reader might easily create an entirely false image of a bleary eyed, rolling drunkard, stumbling through the office door every morning two hours late.

Children

Having two young children will, in Michelle's case at least, make it more difficult for her to gain full-time employment. She makes it very clear that her children are very important to her, and that she presumes they should be of equal interest to the reader of the CV. The truth is that an employer's interest in her children will not go beyond seeing them as a possible obstacle to her time-keeping and regular attendance at work. She has unwittingly made sure that this fear will occur to anyone reading the CV.

There is no need to put children's names in a CV, but their dates of birth *or* ages should be included. In case you are tempted not to mention your children at all on your CV, do bear in mind that, should you be employed on the employer's assumption that you are childless, you run the risk of finding yourself in a job where long hours are expected and no lee-way is given in respect to school holidays, times when your children are home from school due to illness, times when a teacher wishes to see you during working hours, times when school events clash with your work deadlines, times when your mum or partner can't make it to pick the children up from school, and so on and so forth. It is far preferable to be honest from the start and run the risk of not being asked to an interview for a job which would not suit your lifestyle anyway.

What's missing?

There is no Profile, which means that (unless Michelle were sending this CV in response to a specific advertisement) there is no clue whatsoever as to what her career aspirations are. She has not indicated in any way that she has references available, which may cause a suspicious reader to infer that no-one would be willing to give her a good recommendation.

8

THE COVERING LETTER

The importance of a good letter

When replying to an advertisement for a job vacancy, or making a speculative application to a company where you'd like to work, your CV must always be accompanied by an introductory letter. If you are sending a hard copy of your CV, the letter will be printed out (with reference to the suggestions on pages 11 to 13) and sent through the post, or when e-mailing your CV as an attachment, the letter will form the text part of the accompanying e-mail.

The quality of the letter is at least as important as the quality of the CV; in some cases more so. Remember that the letter is the opening shot. It creates the first impression which is the one by which most people judge. An impressive letter can overcome the odd weakness in a CV. Conversely, a poor letter might cause a perfectly good CV to be thrown in the bin.

The correct layout of a formal letter

When setting out a letter, either by hand or in a word-processing program, put your address and today's date in the top right-hand corner (unless you already have your own printed letterheading) and the recipient's name, job title, company name and address below this on the left. Begin with the greeting 'Dear Mr/Mrs/Miss/Ms (surname)' – *not* 'Dear Sir/Madam', which implies that you have not even taken the time to find out the gender of the recruiter, let alone his or her name! At the end of the letter, close with 'Yours sincerely', leave a few lines for your signature, and then type or print your name in full. Use a good quality white paper – as with your CV, avoid coloured paper in case the letter is photocopied later. Do not use the perfumed, flower-embellished stationery your Auntie sent you for your birthday!

Responding to an advertised vacancy

The letter must be short, crisp and clear, opening with the name and date of issue of the publication in which the advertisement appeared, or the website where the job was posted. If a reference number is given, it should be displayed in the top left-hand corner of the letter and, likewise, on the envelope. When responding by e-mail, put the advertised job title and/or reference number in the 'subject' line.

In the second paragraph, say briefly why you believe yourself to be a suitable candidate for the job. The third paragraph should supply routine information, e.g. current rate of pay if the advertisement requests this, period of notice required by your present employer and the length of notice needed to attend an interview.

Example 1 – A Plumber

5 Avenue Road
Anytown
Midshire, XX1 1AA

(Date)

Mr P A Scott-Brown
Adapt Mechanical Services Ltd
118 – 120 Hunts Road
Anytown
Midshire, XX2 1ZZ

Dear Mr Scott-Brown

I am writing in response to your advertisement in the *Construction Gazette* of July 8th for plumbers to work on a Dutch chemical factory contract.

My experience includes work of a similar kind, e.g. the Cann Chemical Factory in Nigeria, for Hull & Blackwell Ltd. Having just completed a hospital building contract in Saudi Arabia as Foreman Plumber with Bates, Barrow (Construction) Ltd, I am now looking for the kind of work offered by your advertisement.

A copy of my CV is enclosed. If you would like to see me for an interview I could attend at short notice.

Yours sincerely

Martin Smith

Example 2 – A Sales Executive

Your Ref: DP 123

5 The Close
Anytown
Midshire, XX1 2AA

(Date)

Mr P R Whiteside
Personnel Manager
Wayside Box & Packaging Co Ltd
6 – 10 Wayside
Anytown
Midshire, XX1 2ZZ

Dear Mr Whiteside

Your advertisement in the *Daily Post* of May 12th for a Regional Sales Manager to increase the rate of business growth in the Southern Counties is of great interest to me.

As you will see from the enclosed CV, I have had extensive experience in negotiating at all levels, including much successful sharp end contact.

Whilst relations with my current employers remain good, the job does not hold the same prospect of advancement that would exist in a larger organisation.

My employers would require one month's notice of leaving. I would appreciate the opportunity of an interview, and it would help if I could have three working days' notice of the date.

Yours sincerely

Cassandra Morris (Miss)

Example 3 – A Secretary/Typist

Your Ref: DG123

29 Brook Avenue
Anytown
Midshire, XX1 3AA

(Date)

Ms Jane Hayward
Neville, Walker & Bates
173 Avondale Road
Anytown
Midshire, XX1 3ZZ

Dear Ms Hayward

I would like to be considered for the position of Secretary/Typist, advertised in the Daily Gazette of April 8th.

A copy of my CV is enclosed. You will see that in addition to my RSA Word Processing Certificate, I do have the required GCSE grades in English and Mathematics. I also have three years' experience as a Secretary/Typist.

Having moved into the area only recently, I am looking for a permanent secretarial job, where the duties and responsibilities would be similar to my last job (salary £xx,xxx).

The opportunity for an interview would be much appreciated, and I could attend at short notice.

Yours sincerely

Shanaz Aslam (Miss)

Although these three specimen letters display the differences in style necessary for different occupations, they should only be viewed as a loose guide. In order to draft an introductory job application letter accurately, you need to have the advertisement in front of you and to refer closely to it.

Speculative job applications

Many job seekers pass the time between applying for advertised vacancies by 'blitzing' companies in a particular field of activity. An advantage of using this tactic is that, once drafted, the same letter can be used repeatedly with one or two minor changes. The disadvantage is that the process amounts to a series of long shots in the dark, and some employers have become ill-disposed to such treatment.

However, if this course of action is to be taken, it must be done properly. The first step is to decide which organisations to approach. Compile an initial list of, say, ten companies. It is important to identify the individual Personnel Manager, Recruiting Officer, Head of Department etc. to which the letter should be addressed. If this is not done, or is done wrongly, the application may not find its way to the right person. Even if it does, he may well not give it as much weight as he would when seeing his name on the envelope, as well as on the letter. A brief telephone call to each of the companies selected is usually all that is necessary, since the receptionist is likely to be able to supply the name and job title of the person who would deal with speculative applications in each particular department. Items for special attention are initials and the correct spelling of names. When writing to a woman, it is best to address her as a 'Ms' if you are not sure whether or not she is married.

The letter itself need be little more than a courteous introduction, with a view to being placed on file.

Example 4 – a speculative application

6 The Avenue
Anytown
Midshire, XX1 4AA

(Date)

Mr J A Smith
Personnel Manager
Wayside Chemical Products Ltd
18 – 22 Wayside
Anytown
Midshire, XX1 4ZZ

Dear Mr Smith

Although you may not have any vacancies at the moment, I am writing to ask if you might keep me in mind for a position as a chemical research analyst, should a vacancy arise in the near future.

The enclosed CV will show that, in addition to possessing the necessary qualifications, I have gained a broad range of experience which I am sure could be used to advantage in working for your company.

My employers require one month's notice of leaving. I would appreciate the opportunity of an interview if a vacancy arises, and five working days' notice would be helpful.

Yours sincerely

Peter Bailey

The pen versus the keyboard

Sometimes, job advertisements will ask you to apply in your own handwriting. The usual response, in this case, is to enclose a handwritten letter with a copy of your CV. Companies may ask you to do this if the job will involve writing documents by hand, but more often they ask for an example of handwriting as your letter will be passed on to a graphologist who can make some assessment of your personality from your handwriting. For this reason, do not ask a friend with clearer handwriting than your own to transcribe the letter for you – no doubt this practice will cause great confusion to the graphologist, especially if your amanuensis is of the opposite sex! In order to get a handwritten letter as neat and straight as possible, place a piece of ruled paper behind the plain sheet of letter paper you are using, and use the lines as guides (do *not* compose the letter itself on lined paper). Write the letter out several times and send the one which you feel looks most suitable. Do not despair if your handwriting is not as beautiful as it could be – just aim for something legible, with no spelling or grammar mistakes. Do not cross out any mistakes you make and do not use correction fluid – if you make an error, start the letter again on a fresh sheet of paper. Try to use a good-quality fountain pen with a smooth nib which suits you – ballpoint pens or, worst of all, pencils, often make your letter and your handwriting look scruffier than it need do. Black or blue ink, from a purely practical point of view, is best for this kind of letter, so save your metallic purple pens for your birthday cards.

If there is no indication as to whether or not the recruiter wants a handwritten letter, it is up to you to decide whether or not it would be preferable to type it on a PC. In the past, covering letters were expected to be written by hand, as an indication of the applicant's standard of handwriting. These days, in most lines of work, it is less important that a worker has clearly legible handwriting as most clerical duties are carried out on a computer. More traditional companies, or those who would be employing you as a secretary, may still like to see that you can write clearly, should you ever need to; however, most will give equal consideration to a letter written using a computer. If your handwriting is really very poor, it is probably best to opt for a wordprocessed version (even if you are applying for a Doctor's position!).

Example 5 – How *not* to write a covering letter

6 Figtree Grove
Anytown
Midshire, XX1 1YY

(Date)

The Manager
Anytown Saw Mills Ltd.
Anytown Industrial Estate
Anytown
Midshire, XX1 1YY

Dear Sir

I hear you are looking for an Office Manager, and I think I could be the man for the job.

The enclosed CV will show you what I am capable of. You will see that I have had wide experience in managing offices in many different industries, and I believe this is the only way to learn.

Living as I do very close to your premises, I would appear to be ideally located, and I should be pleased to attend an interview if you should very kindly invite me to one.

Yours faithfully

Jim Clark

The first mistake Jim has made is to omit the Manager's name – he should have phoned the company and asked for a name before writing the letter. The opening of this letter is *far* too casual. If Jim has heard that there is a job vacancy with the company, he should have located the advertisement and applied in the normal way, quoting the publication in which the advertisement was placed and any reference numbers given. (If he has heard secretly from a friend that there might be a position open but no advertisement has yet been placed, he should try a speculative approach.)

Jim's letter continues in a high-handed manner, telling the reader to see 'what I am capable of' (which, apart from anything else, is poor grammar). He goes on to say, 'I believe this is the only way to learn'. Who does he think he is? This statement clearly implies that the reader would be wrong to disagree, which is not likely to endear him to the potential employer.

In emphasising that his home is near to their place of business, Jim obviously believes this will strengthen his case. The opposite could be just as easily implied. He has made it clear that his main reason for applying is that it would be a convenient place for him to go to work. As his address is already clearly stated in the letter (as it should also be on his CV), Jim should just trust that the Manager has intelligence enough to realise for himself that Jim is a local candidate.

Finally, after sailing through the whole of the letter in this haughty manner, Jim suddenly turns to the other extreme. He starts to crawl, by saying (with regard to an interview), 'if you should very kindly invite me to one'. The reader will be left with an easy decision and this sickening letter will rightly end up in the waste-bin.

APPENDIX

NACRO

Resettlement Plus Helpline in the UK 020 7840 6464 (ex-offenders, their families and friends can call free on 0800 0181 259)

E-mail: helpline@nacro.org.uk

Web: www.nacro.org.uk

INDEX

In the same series

"THE JOB'S YOURS!"

Handbook of a Proven Successful Job Search Strategy

This is a systematic plan for the job seeker. It is a step by step approach whose success has been proved in practice. It tells you exactly what you need to do.

First you must get on that interview shortlist. Next, make sure that you use the interview to your best advantage. Here is where "inside" knowledge helps.

John Waddingham has run a successful Job Club for the unemployed. It is this experience, helping all kinds of people back into – and around – the job market, which is the basis from which he writes.

From his unique vantage point, he knows what methods produce results. He shows how to plan carefully. How to think out applications rigorously. How to prepare for any eventuality. How to excel at the interview. These are the essential ingredients for SUCCESS.

Uniform with this book

In our Right Way Plus series

CAREERING UPWARDS

The Definitive Job-Seeker's Guide to the Selection Process

With greater than ever competition for top jobs, employers are imposing increasingly stringent tests in order to sort the wheat from the chaff in the recruitment process. To the uninitiated, these complicated processes can be baffling: just what are seven point plans, competencies, benchmarking or ''Hygiene'' factors?

Pauline Grant, a business psychologist working in consultancy, knows *exactly* what lies behind the myriad possible components of a modern assessment, and *exactly* what employers and HR staff are looking out for during assessment. She reveals the secrets of tackling psychological testing, assessment centres and interviews with confidence and success. She also offers the benefit of her rich experience in choosing a career path which suits your skills, interests and personality, as well as advising on how to find out which companies are offering the kind of jobs you'd like.

Careering Upwards offers expert and up-to-the-minute advice which new graduates, job-seekers and those wishing to further their career *cannot find elsewhere*.

RW
RIGHT WAY

RW
RIGHT WAY
plus